Science: a second level course

~~wo week~~

~~Earth~~ and Life

Atmosphere, Earth and Life

Prepared for the Course Team by Peter Francis (Chapters 1–8 and 12)
and Nancy Dise (Chapters 9–11)

The Open University

S269 Course Team

Course Team Chair	Peter Francis
Book Chair	Peter Francis
Course Team	Angela Colling
	Nancy Dise
	Steve Drury
	Peter Francis
	Iain Gilmour
	Nigel Harris
	Allister Rees
	Peter Skelton
	Bob Spicer
	Charles Turner
	Chris Wilson
	Ian Wright
	John Wright
Course Managers	Kevin Church
	Annemarie Hedges
Secretaries	Anita Chhabra
	Janet Dryden
	Marilyn Leggett
	Jo Morris
	Rita Quill
	Denise Swann
Series Producer	David Jackson
Editors	Gerry Bearman
	Rebecca Graham
	Kate Richenburg
Graphic Design	Sue Dobson
	Ray Munns
	Pam Owen
	Rob Williams
Liaison Librarian	John Greenwood
Course Assessor	Professor W. G. Chaloner (FRS)

The Open University, Walton Hall, Milton Keynes MK7 6AA

First published 1997

Copyright © 1997 The Open University

Edited, designed and typeset by The Open University.

Printed in the United Kingdom by Jarrold Book Printing, 3 Fison Way, Thetford, Norfolk IP24 IHT

ISBN 0 7492 8184 7

This text forms part of an Open University Second Level Course. If you would like a copy of *Studying with The Open University*, please write to the Course Enquiries Data Service, PO Box 625, Dane Road, Milton Keynes MKI ITY. If you have not enrolled on the Course and would like to buy this or other Open University material, please write to Open University Educational Enterprises Ltd, 12 Cofferidge Close, Stony Stratford, Milton Keynes MKI11BY, United Kingdom.

1.1

S269b3aei1.1

Contents

Preface

A photograph taken from the Space Shuttle showing the Earth, with clouds silhouetted by the Sun against the pearly white, aerosol-rich troposphere. Molecular scattering in the aerosol-free upper atmosphere yields the blue layer.

Of all the inorganic components that make up the Earth System, the atmosphere shows the clearest effects of life. Indeed, some scientists argue that the present atmosphere is a biological artefact, since its composition would have been very different in the absence of life. Furthermore, since the atmosphere is rather tenuous it is relatively easy to change – a fact that we are uncomfortably reminded of in our everyday life, as the concentration of carbon dioxide in the atmosphere increases by a measurable amount each year as a result of human activity.

The consequences for our environment of steadily increasing atmospheric carbon dioxide are difficult to predict, but they are likely to manifest themselves over the next decades and centuries. In this book, we examine the atmosphere over a much longer time-scale, tracing its evolution since the origin of the Earth. This will enable you to evaluate current changes in the broader context of changes that have taken place in the past.

Of the various gases present in the atmosphere, we examine only two in detail – oxygen and carbon dioxide. Oxygen is a major constituent of the atmosphere today, comprising 21% by volume. Virtually all atmospheric oxygen is of biological origin – it is only found in trace amounts in the atmospheres of some other planets in the Solar System. Carbon dioxide, on the other hand, dominates the atmospheres of our neighbouring planets but is present only in trace amounts in the Earth's modern atmosphere. Nonetheless, carbon dioxide has played a major role in the evolution of the Earth System.

We begin this book with a quantitative assessment of the size of the atmosphere relative to the other components of the Earth System, and particularly of the sizes of the various reservoirs of oxygen on Earth. We then review the process of photosynthesis that has been responsible for the formation of atmospheric oxygen. While it is easy enough to identify photosynthesis as a *source* of oxygen, the processes that have permitted oxygen to accumulate in the atmosphere, and have maintained it at its present level of about 21%, are far more subtle.

We shall examine fairly straightforward lines of evidence preserved in the fossil and rock records to deduce atmospheric oxygen concentrations throughout the Earth's history. This exercise provides useful insights into the processes, sources and sinks that have governed atmospheric oxygen levels throughout geological time. After examining the geological record, we test our understanding of the processes controlling oxygen levels by modelling the atmospheric oxygen level for different periods in the Earth's history. Comparing the results of the models with the direct evidence gives reasonable agreement, suggesting that we have a fairly good understanding of the overall long-term processes controlling atmospheric oxygen. The level of atmospheric oxygen has been remarkably stable over the last several hundred million years at a level conducive to the persistence of a diverse and complex biosphere. We examine the role that life itself may have played in the regulatory processes.

In the second part of the book we turn our attention to carbon dioxide, a gas which, like oxygen, plays a critical role in biological processes, but in addition is central to the regulation of the Earth's surface temperature. As with oxygen, we examine the geological record of past carbon dioxide levels, and then study how these levels can be modelled from reasonable inferences of contemporary geological parameters. Because atmospheric carbon dioxide is a major influence on the Earth's surface temperature, we also review evidence as to how temperature has varied in the past, and consider feedback links between temperature and processes that provide either sources or sinks for carbon dioxide. Modelling the climatic response to currently increasing atmospheric carbon dioxide levels is of immediate practical concern to us all. The focus on modelling adopted in this part of the book is intended both to highlight the usefulness of modelling and to identify some of the problems and pitfalls involved. Some of these models are necessarily more speculative than others: we encourage you to read them critically, and to form your own opinions about their merits.

In this book you will encounter some topics that you have met elsewhere in the Course. This is in part a consequence of the way that different authors have approached topics, but it is also in part a deliberate strategy. Not only does re-visiting a topic reinforce the understanding of it, but it also emphasizes that the same subject can have different relevance in different contexts. And sometimes, there is just plain disagreement, not only about deeper concepts like how the Earth System has evolved, but also about some 'simple' parameters like the sizes of individual sources and sinks for atmospheric gases. Where possible, we have drawn attention to these disagreements, but you should be prepared to find in your broader reading different interpretations of the topics we have discussed, and even different values for the same parameters. We hope that Earth and Life will help you to better evaluate some of these issues, and to form your own judgements.

Chapter I
Oxygen and the Earth

1.1 Introduction

Oxygen is important to all of us. Without oxygen, each and every one of us would have only minutes to live. Its importance in sustaining life is so great that it is entrenched in a popular political metaphor which speaks of denying the 'oxygen of publicity' to terrorists. Long before oxygen had been isolated and its chemistry worked out, Greek philosophers (in particular, Aristotle) recognized four 'elements' – air, fire, water and earth. Oxygen plays an important role in each of these. The Earth's atmosphere, commonly referred to as air, contains about 21% of oxygen by volume. Oxygen is essential for fires to burn. Water contains oxygen in a combined form, with one atom of oxygen being linked to two atoms of hydrogen to form H_2O – the one chemical formula that is recognized by even the least scientifically inclined. It is less well known that oxygen is one of the most abundant elements in the composition of the solid parts of the Earth: rocks are made up of complex minerals containing silicon, oxygen and metallic elements, while most sand consists of a compond known as silica, SiO_2, which is silicon and oxygen in simple combination.

It was not until the 18th century that the existence of an element such as oxygen was first postulated. Scientists in a number of countries carried out experiments on combustion and respiration, and recognized, among other things, that a mouse placed in a sealed jar would die once a candle had burned out in the jar. For a while, the early investigators were side-tracked into believing that substances which burn contain an entity known as *phlogiston*. Although Joseph Priestly and Carl Scheele were the first to discover oxygen, in 1772, it was the great French chemist Antoine Lavoisier (1749–94) who explained the true nature of combustion and gave the vital invisible gas, which he identified as essential for combustion, the name *oxygène*. He compounded the name from a Greek root, *oxus*, meaning sour or sharp because he thought (wrongly) that oxygen was essential in the formation of acids.

As oxygen is so important, we start by looking at how much of it there is in the atmosphere, the oceans and the solid Earth (see Box 1.1). We shall then, in Chapter 2, review the reactivity of oxygen and consider oxygen's role in life on Earth. In Chapters 3 and 4 we consider how the amount of oxygen in the Earth's atmosphere has varied through geological time. Later, in Chapters 5 to 8, we examine the role of life in generating an oxygen-rich atmosphere on the early Earth, and in subsequently maintaining the oxygen content at a level suitable for complex life-forms to flourish. In the second half of this book (Chapters 9 to 12) we turn our attention to another important atmospheric gas – carbon dioxide.

1.2 How much oxygen is there?

The atmosphere, the oceans and the solid Earth (and the biosphere) can each be regarded as a reservoir of oxygen. Some of the oxygen in these reservoirs is in the molecular form as O_2, and some is present in combination with atoms of other elements in the form of compounds such as water. (Another form of molecular oxygen is ozone, but we will not consider this until later in this book.) We are particularly interested in the amounts of molecular oxygen (i.e. uncombined oxygen)

Box 1.1 Terminology

We use the following terminology throughout this book.

'The Earth' means the entire planet Earth, i.e. not only the solid Earth but also the hydrosphere, atmosphere and biosphere.

The 'solid Earth' refers to the core, mantle and crust only.

The 'atmosphere' means the envelope of gases surrounding the Earth and extending out into space.

The 'hydrosphere' is used to describe the oceans, rivers, lakes and all other bodies of liquid water on the Earth, as well as the ice-caps. (Because the oceans contain 96% of all the water

on Earth, in our discussions and calculations we shall generally ignore the fresh water contained in the lakes, rivers and ice-caps.)

The 'biosphere' encompasses *all* the organisms living on the Earth's surface, and in the hydrosphere and the atmosphere. It includes

all forms of bacterial life, plant life, and animal life.

'Rocks' means the silicate minerals, carbonate minerals, etc. that make up the crust and solid parts of the mantle.

---

that are present, as it is this oxygen that is needed for respiration and which therefore supports life. But so that you can appreciate the omnipresence of the element oxygen on Earth, we shall also consider the oxygen that is present in combined form in compounds such as the water in the oceans, and the silicates in the rocks. To distinguish such oxygen from molecular oxygen, we shall refer to it as combined oxygen.

Let us focus first on the molecular oxygen in the atmosphere. The mass of a column of atmosphere with a cross-sectional area of one square metre, extending from the surface of the Earth all the way up to space is 1.03×10^4 kg. Since the Earth's surface area is 5.1×10^{14} m^2, this means that the total mass of the atmosphere is: 1.03×10^4 kg m$^{-2} \times 5.1 \times 10^{14}$ m$^2 = 5.3 \times 10^{18}$ kg. (This column mass relates directly to atmospheric pressure. If you want to know more about atmospheric pressure, read Box 1.2.)

■   If the Earth's atmosphere is about of 21% by volume of oxygen (Table 1.1), what is the mass of the oxygen in the atmosphere?

This apparently straightforward question conceals a complication. You might expect that you could do a simple percentage calculation, finding out what 21% of

Table 1.1   Average composition of the atmosphere (excluding water vapour and pollutants which vary from place to place).

Gas	Abundance (% by volume)*
nitrogen, N_2	78.1
oxygen, O_2	20.9
argon, Ar	0.93
carbon dioxide, CO_2	$0.036 = 360$ p.p.m.[†]
neon, Ne	$1.8 \times 10^{-3} = 18$ p.p.m.
helium, He	$5.2 \times 10^{-4} = 5.2$ p.p.m.
methane, CH_4	$2 \times 10^{-4} = 2$ p.p.m.
krypton, Kr	$1 \times 10^{-4} = 1$ p.p.m.
hydrogen, H_2	$5 \times 10^{-5} = 0.5$ p.p.m.
nitrous oxide, N_2O	$3.2 \times 10^{-5} = 0.32$ p.p.m.
xenon, Xe	$9 \times 10^{-6} = 0.09$ p.p.m.
ozone, O_3	$1 \times 10^{-6} - 1 \times 10^{-5} = 0.01 - 0.1$ p.p.m.

*Gases which are present in trace amounts are commonly recorded in parts per million (p.p.m.). These are only approximate values as the concentrations can vary. The water content may vary from zero to 4%.

[†]1996 value. This is increasing by 1–2 p.p.m. annually.

Box 1.2 Quantifying gases

Atmospheric pressure

The mass of a vertical column of the atmosphere (with a cross-sectional area of $1\,m^2$) extending from the surface of the Earth (i.e. sea-level) all the way up to space (taken to be the 'top' of the atmosphere) is $10\,339\,kg$; this is known as the **column mass**. To express this column mass per unit area in the more familiar units of pressure (defined as force per unit area) we need to convert the mass into a force. This is done by multiplying the mass by the acceleration due to gravity g ($9.8\,m\,s^{-2}$), thus:

the force exerted by a column of atmosphere with a cross-sectional area of $1\,m^2$

$= 10\,339\,kg \times 9.8\,m\,s^{-2} = 1.013 \times 10^5\,kg\,m\,s^{-2}$

$= 1.013 \times 10^5\,N$

Therefore the atmospheric pressure at sea-level is $1.013 \times 10^5\,N\,m^{-2}$, or $1.013 \times 10^5\,Pa$ (Pa stands for pascal, the SI unit of pressure).

Some atmospheric scientists have not adopted the SI unit of pressure; instead they use the bar (from the Greek *baros*, meaning weight) and millibar (mbar), where $1\,mbar = 10^2\,Pa$. Hence you will often see atmospheric pressure given in millibars – at sea-level it is $1013\,mbar$.

It is important that you understand the difference between column mass per unit area and atmospheric pressure – a difference analogous to the difference between mass and weight. It is best understood in a planetary context: if one could take a column of the Earth's atmosphere to Mars, it would still have a *mass* of $10\,339\,kg$, but it would exert a much lower *pressure* there because of Mars' lower surface gravity.

Partial pressure

It is also important to distinguish between atmospheric pressure (the pressure at the surface of the Earth due to the mass of the overlying atmosphere) and the pressure of a gas in a sealed container. If one were to launch a strong container (such as the Space Shuttle) into space, the gases inside it would exert a pressure on the walls of the vessel, and that pressure would be the same in space as it was on the launch pad, although in space the gas would be weightless, along with the crew and everything else on board.

The pressure of the gas would be dictated by the number of gas molecules present and their temperature.

For air (or any mixture of gases) in a sealed container, the contribution to the total pressure P_{total} made by each gas would be given by:

$$P_{total} = P_{N_2} + P_{O_2} + P_{CO_2} + \dots$$

where P_{N_2}, P_{O_2}, P_{CO_2}, etc. are the *partial pressures* of the gases N_2, O_2, CO_2, etc., respectively. The partial pressure is the pressure that the particular gas would exert if it were present in the absence of the other gases.

To calculate the partial pressure of carbon dioxide in a sealed volume of atmospheric air, we multiply the value of atmospheric pressure by a quantity called the **volume mixing ratio** or volume fraction, which is the ratio of the number of molecules of a gas to the total number of molecules of all gases in the sample. There are about 360 p.p.m. of carbon dioxide in the present-day atmosphere – this is the volume mixing ratio. Therefore the partial pressure of carbon dioxide is $1.013\,bar \times 360 \times 10^{-6}$, which is equal to $3.6 \times 10^{-4}\,bar$, i.e. $0.36\,mbar$.

Now, the contribution made to total *atmospheric* pressure by a gas depends, among other things, on its mass, which in turn depends on its relative molecular mass and on the amount of the gas present (i.e. the **mass mixing ratio** or mass fraction). To make the calculation relatively simple, we shall assume that, besides oxygen, the remaining volume of the atmosphere (about 79%) is occupied by nitrogen molecules (this is only an approximation as you can see from Table 1.1). The relative molecular mass of oxygen (O_2) is 32, whereas that for nitrogen (N_2) is 28, therefore the mean relative molecular mass of the molecules in the atmosphere is about

$$\left(32 \times \frac{21}{100}\right) + \left(28 \times \frac{79}{100}\right) = 28.8, \text{ or } 29$$

If we were to replace each and every molecule in the present atmosphere by a carbon dioxide molecule (mean relative molecular mass of $12 + (2 \times 16) = 44$), then atmospheric pressure would increase by a factor of roughly $44/29$. However, if we wished to retain the same pressure using only carbon dioxide, we would have to reduce the number of molecules.

the mass of the atmosphere is and so come up with the answer, just as you can do when considering the percentage composition by volume, i.e. the volume fraction or volume mixing ratio (see Box 1.2), because in the latter case you can reasonably assume that the molecules of the various gases in the atmosphere occupy the same volume under the same conditions.

However, the same is not true for mass: the molecules of different gases have *different* relative molecular masses, and this has to be taken into account when calculating the percentage composition by mass, i.e. the mass fraction or mass mixing ratio. If the mean relative molecular mass of the molecules in the atmosphere is 29 (see Box 1.2), the mass fraction or mass mixing ratio of oxygen is about $21\% \times (32/29) = 23\%$. (Of course, if the composition of the atmosphere changes, so will the mean relative molecular mass.) Thus, if the total mass of all the molecules in the atmosphere is 5.3×10^{18} kg, the mass of molecular oxygen present is 5.3×10^{18} kg $\times 0.21 \times (32/29)$, or about 1.2×10^{18} kg. Oxygen is also present in the atmosphere in its combined form – in water vapour (H_2O) and in gases such as CO_2, as you saw in Table 1.1.

How does the amount of oxygen in the atmosphere compare with the amount of oxygen in the oceans? For sustaining life, there is, of course, a huge difference between the oceanic and atmospheric oxygen reservoirs: atmospheric oxygen is mostly in the form of a molecular gas (O_2) – uncombined and available for breathing, whereas the oxygen in the oceans is, for the most part, present as a constituent of water and so is not readily available.

What is the size of the oxygen reservoir in the ocean? Because the oceans are so vast they contain a great deal of oxygen. As one molecule of water consists of two atoms of hydrogen (relative atomic mass 1.0) and one atom of oxygen (relative atomic mass 16), the relative molecular mass of water is $(2 \times 1.0) + 16 = 18$, and hence oxygen constitutes 16/18ths (i.e. 89%) of the mass of one molecule of water. Now, the mass of a given amount of water is the mass of all the molecules in it, so oxygen must constitute 89% of that mass.

▨   What is the mass of oxygen in the oceans? You need the following information for this calculation: oceans cover 70% of the surface of the Earth; an area of 3.6×10^8 km^2, and have an average depth of 3.65 km; 1 m^3 of ocean has a mass of 1000 kg, if it is regarded as pure water.

▨   The oceans have a volume of 1.3×10^9 km^3, i.e. 1.3×10^{18} m^3, and therefore have a mass of 1.3×10^{21} kg. Now 89% of the mass of the oceans is due to the oxygen present in water molecules. Therefore there are $(89/100) \times 1.3 \times 10^{21}$ kg of oxygen (in combined form) in the oceans, i.e. 1.2×10^{21} kg.

The oceans also contain a tiny proportion – about 6 p.p.m. on average – of dissolved oxygen gas (molecular oxygen), which *is* available for respiration. It is this much smaller oxygen reservoir that supports the teeming life in the oceans.

▨   What is the mass of available, dissolved oxygen in the oceans?

▨   If the mass of the oceans is 1.3×10^{21} kg, and they contain 6 p.p.m. (6×10^{-6}) of molecular oxygen, then the mass of available oxygen is $1.3 \times 10^{21} \times 6 \times 10^{-6}$ kg or 7.8×10^{15} kg.

We shall now see how the mass of oxygen in the atmosphere and in the oceans compares with the amount of oxygen in the solid Earth.

Geophysicists have shown that the solid Earth has an innermost metallic core overlain by a mantle of dense rocky material, covered by a thin skin of lower density rocks which constitutes the crust (Figure 1.1). If we consider the solid Earth in its entirety – including its core – then iron is the only element that is more abundant by mass than oxygen; however, if we consider just the Earth's crust, then oxygen is *the* most abundant element (Table 1.2).

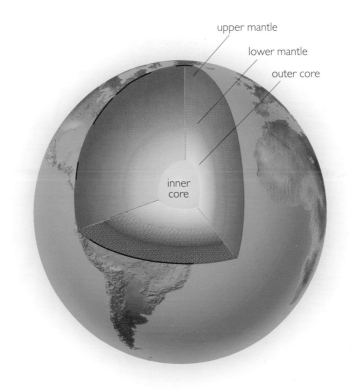

upper mantle
lower mantle
outer core
inner core

Figure 1.1
A cross-section through the Earth, illustrating the various layers of the solid Earth.

Table 1.2 Relative abundance by mass of elements in the solid Earth and in the Earth's crust.

Element	Solid Earth (mass %)	Earth's crust (mass %)
iron	35	6
oxygen	30	46
silicon	15	28
magnesium	13	4.0
nickel	2.4	trace
sulfur	1.9	trace
calcium	1.1	2.4
aluminium	1.1	8.0
potassium	trace	2.3
sodium	trace	2.1
other	<1.0	<1.0

Physicists have calculated, from observations such as the gravitational effects of the Earth on the Moon, that the mass of the Earth is about 6×10^{24} kg. Using this value and the figure in Table 1.2, we can work out that there are about 1.8×10^{24} kg of (combined) oxygen in the solid Earth.

We summarize our findings about the sizes of the various oxygen reservoirs on the Earth in Table 1.3. Although rough, these estimates show that the amount of oxygen available to support life in the atmosphere and in the oceans is remarkably small on a planetary scale. As we progress further, the smallness and vulnerability of these reservoirs of available oxygen will become much more apparent. It is the molecular oxygen (whether it is present in the atmosphere or oceans) that is available for respiration and therefore life. We shall take a closer look at this in Chapter 2.

Table 1.3 Amounts of oxygen in the three main oxygen reservoirs on Earth.

Oxygen reservoir	Mass of oxygen/kg
atmosphere	1.2×10^{18} (molecular gas, available for respiration)
oceans	7.8×10^{15} (dissolved molecular gas, available for respiration)
	1.2×10^{21} (combined as H_2O, not available for respiration)
solid Earth	2×10^{24} (combined, not available for respiration)

1.3 Summary of Chapter 1

1   The Earth contains a large amount of oxygen, some in molecular form, O_2, which supports life, and some in combined form in compounds.

2   There are two reservoirs containing 'free' molecular oxygen available for respiration: the atmosphere and the oceans. The atmosphere contains about 1.2×10^{18} kg of molecular oxygen; the oceans contain 7.8×10^{15} kg.

3   The oceans contain about 1.2×10^{21} kg of oxygen combined with hydrogen as water, H_2O.

4   The solid Earth consists of about 30% oxygen, combined in the form of minerals. There are about 2×10^{24} kg oxygen in combined form in the solid Earth.

Chapter 2
Oxygen and life

2.1 The role of oxygen – an overview

Oxygen plays a pivotal role in life on Earth. It is a component of all living things – a constituent of the molecules that are the building blocks of life. So all biological matter, living or dead – in other words, all biomass – contains combined oxygen.

Oxygen is also a key part of the mechanisms that sustain plant and animal life – photosynthesis and respiration. It is the subtle balance between the consumption of oxygen in respiration and its production in photosynthesis that is critical for the stability of the oxygen level in the Earth's atmosphere. We explore this very important matter further in subsequent chapters.

In this chapter we start by looking at some of the general properties of oxygen (Section 2.2) before considering oxygen in the context of respiration (Section 2.3) and photosynthesis (Section 2.4).

2.2 Reactivity of oxygen

Oxygen is a paradoxical substance. We suffocate if the air we breathe contains less than about 5–10% of oxygen but, chemically, oxygen is such a vigorously reactive substance that it is potentially destructive. Industry spends billions of pounds every year trying to prevent rusting – a reaction between iron and oxygen – from taking place: for instance, an unpainted car would become a useless heap of rust in a year or two. In equation form, rusting is:

$$\underbrace{4Fe}_{\substack{\text{metallic}\\\text{iron}}} + \underbrace{3O_2}_{\substack{\text{from the}\\\text{atmosphere}}} \longrightarrow \underbrace{2Fe_2O_3}_{\substack{\text{expensive}\\\text{red stains}}} \qquad \text{(Equation 2.1)}$$

(In detail, rusting is far more complex than this equation implies, and rust itself contains some combined water – as you shall see in Chapter 4. You will know from experience that water promotes rusting, although it has been omitted from the equation above.)

Liquid oxygen forms an essential component of rocket fuel: it is so reactive (and potentially dangerous) that engineers treat it with extreme caution. Free oxygen atoms would be as almost dangerous to us as rocket fuel, damaging the cells in our bodies. To counteract this, once oxygen enters our bloodstream, its molecules are 'locked away' in an iron-rich protein in the blood, known as **haemoglobin**. In this form, it can circulate through the body and fuel metabolic processes effectively.

Perhaps one of the most dramatic manifestations of the reactivity of oxygen is combustion. It takes many forms, but all involve a reaction in which a substance (element or compound) combines with oxygen and, as a result energy is liberated.

As we have seen elsewhere in the Course, if one were to be so extravagant as to burn a diamond, the reaction could be represented by the equation:

$$C + O_2 \longrightarrow CO_2 + energy \qquad \text{(Equation 2.2)}$$

Burning of wood, paper, coal and oil are all more complex examples of the same process. Iron itself will burn in the right circumstances, for instance when it is finely divided; thus wire wool will burn quite vigorously, producing a shower of sparks. (Fortunately, it is not so easy to get the sheet metal of a car to ignite!) Combustion is an example of a type of reaction known as oxidation. If you want to refresh your memory about oxidation and the reverse reaction, reduction, see Box 2.1.

Fire has played an essential role in human development. Fire *may* also have played a role in the evolution of the Earth's atmosphere. But how? Every year bolts of lightning start innumerable forest fires all over the world – they are a normal part of forest ecology. However, if the atmospheric oxygen content were only a few per cent higher, the effects of forest fires would be catastrophic – they would start much more easily, burn more fiercely, and would be unstoppable, even in humid areas. Forests, as we know them, could not exist. Some scientists have speculated that forest fires provide a practical limit, or *buffer*, to the oxygen content of the atmosphere. (We shall return to this idea in Chapter 7.)

Oxygen, then, is a reactive element, ever ready to combine with other elements through oxidation reactions, which sometimes occur as combustion or fire. It may therefore seem surprising that oxygen can exist in the atmosphere at all. That it does is an expression of a highly unusual aspect of the Earth as a planet: some process must be constantly at work on Earth to replenish the oxygen, because oxygen is always so ready to combine with other materials that it would otherwise be entirely consumed. It was this realization that led James Lovelock to a perceptive insight into how life could affect planetary atmospheres. While seeking evidence for life on Mars for NASA in the 1960s, Lovelock realized that the Earth's atmosphere is unstable and reactive because it contains abundant oxygen and traces of methane, whereas the atmosphere of Mars is *inert,* consisting mostly of carbon dioxide. He argued that because Earth's oxygen-rich atmosphere is so reactive, it could only be sustained through the metabolism of the life on the planet, whereas Mars' inert atmosphere is in equilibrium, indicating that no such processes are at work, and that life must now be absent there. His conclusion was vindicated when the Viking spacecraft landed on Mars in 1976, and found no trace of living organisms.

The influence of life on the Earth's oxygen supply is an idea that we have already visited in this Course. The key points are: first, without *life*, the Earth would have no molecular oxygen; and second, oxygen cannot be considered in isolation – its role can only be understood as part of the workings of the entire Earth System. In particular, the story of oxygen is inextricably intertwined with the story of the carbon cycle, which is central to interactions between Earth and life. A summary of the carbon cycle is shown in Figure 2.1. This illustration is a simplification of the various interlinking cycles that make up the carbon cycle on Earth, but it is in sufficient detail for present purposes.

2.3 Respiration and the Earth's oxygen inventory

On a planetary scale, atmospheric oxygen is small beer, as the arithmetic in Section 1.2 demonstrated. Let us look at this further, in terms of the oxidation of food which occurs during aerobic respiration. Of course, food is biomass and when animals digest biomass it is oxidized, and, as a result energy and carbon dioxide are liberated. As we have seen elsewhere in the Course, we can represent this process in its simplest form by Equation 2.3:

$$\underbrace{(CH_2O)_n}_{\text{biomass}} + \underbrace{nO_2}_{\substack{\text{in the} \\ \text{atmosphere}}} \longrightarrow nH_2O + \underbrace{nCO_2}_{\text{gas}} + \text{energy} \qquad \text{(Equation 2.3)}$$

Box 2.1 Oxidation and reduction

The addition of oxygen to an element or compound constitutes a very important chemical process, known as **oxidation**. Oxidation reactions tend to release energy. Strictly speaking, oxidation is concerned with the loss of electrons from atoms or ions, and it need not involve oxygen at all; however, since oxygen readily accepts electrons, the general process of electron transfer away from an atom, or ion, has come to be known as oxidation. The reverse process, the gain of electrons by an atom or ion, which often involves the removal of oxygen from a compound, has a less self-evident

name: **reduction**. Rusting is an example of oxidation, while reduction is what happens when iron oxide ores (chemically similar to rust) are smelted to form iron. An **oxidizing** environment is one that tends to promote oxidation, and a **reducing** one inhibits it.

Oxidation takes place in many different circumstances. When petrol undergoes combustion in a car engine, it is oxidized, forming mostly carbon dioxide and water (which are expelled from the exhaust) and producing energy to power the car. When we eat food – in effect our fuel – oxidation takes place as the food is eventually oxidized by respiration, yielding carbon dioxide, water, energy – and

a range of less savoury products. This conversion of food is called **aerobic respiration**.

Oxidation can also take place in environments where oxygen does not appear to be available, such as when iron rusts under water.

■ Oxidation in air is relatively straightforward. But why should iron rust in water, out of contact with the air?

■ As we noted earlier in Chapter 1, water usually contains dissolved oxygen. Although dissolved and present in small amounts, it remains chemically potent.

(It is essential to stress the solubility of oxygen in water – a fact amply demonstrated by a contented goldfish swimming in a bowl. Much of our discussion about life and oxygen will be concerned with life in the oceans, rather than on land, so dissolved oxygen is of special significance.)

In the natural world, reduction is a less visible process than oxidation, but it is nevertheless important. Reduction takes place in **anoxic** (oxygen-poor) environments, such as the foetid black muds at the bottom of stagnant lakes, from which all the dissolved oxygen has been extracted, and where lack of circulation prevents the mixing-in of oxygenated water.

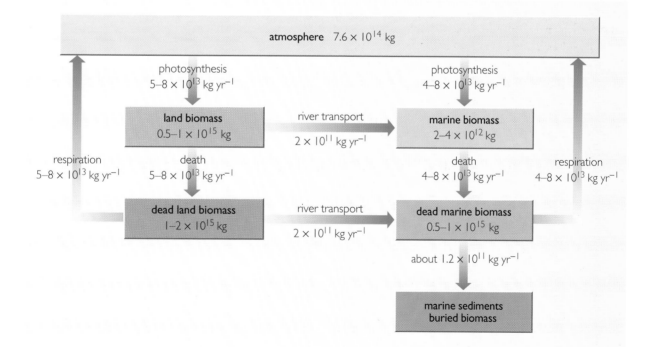

Figure 2.1

A summary of the biological parts of the carbon cycle, showing estimates of the sizes of the main reservoirs of carbon (expressed in kg of carbon) and the fluxes from one reservoir to another. (For a discussion of biomass, see Box 2.2.)

For humans, food is edible biomass (e.g. carbohydrates such as pasta). No flames accompany the oxidation of biomass during respiration, but our bodies are kept warm by the energy liberated. Now Equation 2.3 shows that every atom of carbon in biomass requires one molecule of oxygen for the oxidation process. Adding up the relative atomic masses of the basic biomass unit and molecular oxygen ($C = 12$, $H = 1.0$, $O = 16$; $CH_2O = 12 + (2 \times 1.0) + 16 = 30$ and $O_2 = 32$, respectively), we find that 30 units of biomass require 32 units of oxygen for oxidation.

- If you assume that every human metabolizes 0.25 kg (dry mass) of biomass (e.g. carbohydrates in the form of pasta) per day, how much oxygen does he/she consume, and how much carbon dioxide is liberated?

- If 30 units of biomass require 32 units of oxygen for oxidation, 1 unit of biomass will require (32/30) units of oxygen. Therefore, $(32/30) \times 0.25$ kg, i.e. 0.27 kg of oxygen will be consumed by each human being in a day. Similarly, as the relative molecular mass of carbon dioxide is $12 + (2 \times 16) = 44$, it follows that $(44/30) \times 0.25$ kg $= 0.36$ kg of carbon dioxide will be liberated.

If the world population is taken to be 5 billion (5×10^9), then the total amount of oxygen consumed by all humans in a day will be roughly $0.27 \times 5 \times 10^9$ kg, i.e. 1.35×10^9 kg day^{-1}.

- If we continue to consider only the human population, how long would it take us, at this rate, to use up all the oxygen in the Earth's atmosphere?

- There are 365 days in a year, so the yearly consumption of oxygen would be $365 \times 1.35 \times 10^9$ kg, i.e. 4.9×10^{11} kg. We established earlier (in Section 1.2) that there are 1.2×10^{18} kg of molecular oxygen in the atmosphere, so at this rate all the oxygen would be consumed in $(1.2 \times 10^{18})/(4.9 \times 10^{11})$ years, or roughly 2.4 million years.

Now, 2.4 million years sounds a long time, but it is trivial in terms of the age of the Earth, which is 4.6 *billion* (4600 million) years. Thus, at present population levels, we could breathe our way through a complete atmosphere's worth of oxygen in a relatively short time geologically speaking. Humans, of course, are not the only consumers of oxygen. Apart from all the other air-breathing animals on land and the oxygen-respiring fish in the sea, there are many other ways in which oxygen is consumed, e.g. in forest fires and in the combustion of fossil fuels. There are also some major geological processes, such as weathering, that consume oxygen; we shall explore these later. If one adds up all the metabolic activities of *all* the life-forms on Earth, the residence time of oxygen in the atmosphere appears to be only a few thousand years.

From the calculations above, you can see that the amount of oxygen in the atmosphere is surprisingly small and it could be completely used up in a relatively short time. So, without renewable sources of oxygen we – and all the other animals – could not exist. A thought-provoking analogy can be drawn here between 'Spaceship Earth' and a cruise ship equipped with desalination equipment to provide fresh water. If you set sail on the ship for a cruise of one year's duration, you might be worried if you knew that the vessel only had a reserve of a few minute's worth of fresh water at any one time. But this is effectively the situation that has prevailed with the Earth's oxygen supply over the last 600 million years. In later chapters, we shall examine how this precarious balance has been maintained.

Box 2.2 Biomass

When one contemplates life on Earth, it is easy to be overwhelmed by its infinite diversity (Figure 2.2). But this apparently boundless variety disappears when one looks at life in chemical terms. *All* plants, for example, are composed of carbon, hydrogen and oxygen, plus a few other elements such as nitrogen, so daisies and oak trees are barely distinguishable in terms of their component elements. Animals are not much different, except for some additional nitrogen, and a little extra phosphorus and calcium in their bones (as you can see from Table 2.1). In fact, all the glorious diversity of life can be effectively summarized by a single chemical formula $(CH_2O)_n$, where n is a whole number. Approximating the composition of living material to $(CH_2O)_n$ will allow us to reach some highly significant conclusions later. The term **biomass** is used to describe a given amount of $(CH_2O)_n$ (whether living or dead), and it is usually expressed in units of dry material. There

Table 2.1 Chemical composition of a dried Open University student and a dried green plant (alfalfa).

Element	Dried OU student (mass %) (estimated)	Dried alfalfa (mass %) (measured)
carbon	48.4	45.4
oxygen	23.7	41.0
nitrogen	13.0	3.3
hydrogen	6.6	5.5
calcium	3.5	2.3
phosphorous	1.6	0.28
sulfur	1.6	0.44
sodium	0.6	0.16
potassium	0.5	0.91

is little actual CH_2O in the real world (CH_2O is an unpleasant but useful compound called methanal or formaldehyde), but there is plenty of $(CH_2O)_6$, which is a sugar called glucose (usually written $C_6H_{12}O_6$). For present purposes, one can think of $(CH_2O)_n$ as being synonymous with carbohydrates.

There is a lot of biomass about. Oak trees, daisies, grass, whales, slugs, algae, nuts, snakes, corn and you, gentle reader, all form part of the Earth's living biomass. It has been estimated that there are about 1.8 million named species of living organisms, and probably many more

times that number which remain to be discovered and named. Most of this diversity arises from the animal world – for instance, there are far more species of beetle than of any other group. However, in terms of *total mass*, plant life is far more important. Although beetles are incredibly numerous, they are individually tiny; their total mass is negligible in comparison with the total mass of all the trees on Earth. Thus, most of the Earth's living biomass occurs in vast forests, notably tropical rain forests and sub-Arctic coniferous forests. 'Spaceship Earth's' most appealing passengers are its large

animals such as elephants and whales. While these endangered species are important in cultural terms, large animals are negligible in terms of biomass. Our concerns will be mostly with the simplest organisms, such as bacteria which form an abundant, living component in soils and leaf moulds, breaking down the organic material. These tiny single-celled organisms also abound within larger organisms, where they fulfil vital metabolic roles.

Although notoriously difficult to quantify, it has been estimated that there are about 2×10^{15} kg of living biomass on dry land, mostly constituted by forests (calculated as $(CH_2O)_n$). One complication in making this estimate lies in determining what is actually 'living'. Consider the giant Californian redwood tree, *Sequoia gigantea*. These noble trees rise more than 100 m above the forest floor and weigh more than 2000 tonnes. Some are more than 3000 years old. Standing on the forest floor (continued overleaf)

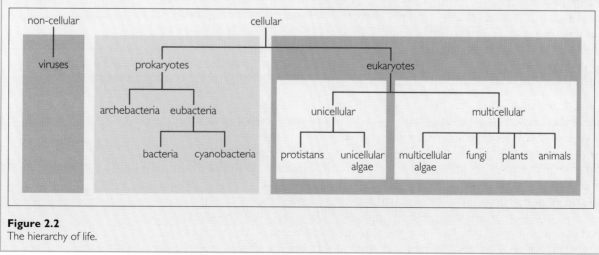

Figure 2.2
The hierarchy of life.

and looking up at a redwood, no-one would doubt that it was 'alive'. Yet both the exterior bark and the interior solid wood are dead – the only truly living parts are the leaves, flowers and seeds, and a layer of living cells immediately beneath the bark: these parts collectively form only about 3% of the total mass of the redwood tree!

It is thought that there are about 7×10^{12} kg of living biomass in the oceans (calculated as $(CH_2O)_n$). The amount of biomass represented by visible organisms such as fish is negligible; the microscopic plankton that drift in the water are far more significant. There are many different kinds of plankton: phytoplankton are autotrophic (like plants, they use solar energy in a photosynthetic process to derive their sustenance from the inorganic, abiogenic, world); whereas zooplankton are heterotrophic, feeding on other organisms. Phytoplankton biomass far exceeds that of all marine animal life; indeed, 'blooms' of phytoplankton are abundant enough to colour the ocean when seen from space, and they have been called the 'meadows of the oceans' (Figures 2.3 and 2.4).

Although the amount of living biomass in the oceans is only about 0.4% of that on dry land, it nonetheless plays an decisive role in the global cycles of carbon and oxygen.

Figure 2.3
Nimbus-7 satellite view of the north-west coast of Scotland and the Outer Hebrides, recorded in May 1980, showing the scale of plankton blooms: the diffuse area west of the Hebrides is not cloud, but a vast expanse of plankton.

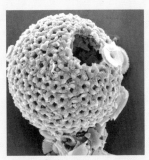

(a)   6.0 μm

(b)   1.2 μm

Figure 2.4
(a) The spherical 'skeleton' of a calcium-secreting dinoflagellate (a phytoplankton).
(b) A close-up detail of coccoliths on the surface of a coccosphere. The individual coccoliths are 1.5 μm across.

■ Why should such small amounts of biomass be so influential compared with the enormous masses of the forests?

■ Planktonic organisms have short life cycles, whereas trees may live for centuries. Thus, plankton respond far more quickly to changes in conditions than forests do, so leading to a rapid turnover in the materials that they consume and produce.

In fact, when the combinations of temperature and nutrient supply are right, plankton can multiply so prodigiously that they drastically modify the surface ocean environment.

Importantly, there are also large reservoirs of 'dead' biomass which is buried and remains undecayed. Examples of such biomass are the organic matter disseminated throughout soils, and peat, the accumulated remains of plant material that lived and died in shallow bogs and swamps. There is probably about twice as much dead biomass on land as living biomass, while in the oceans, dead biomass is even more predominant: there are probably several hundred times more dead biomass than living, because the dead material accumulates on the sea floor. There are also large reservoirs of **fossil carbon**, contained in coal and petroleum deposits, the so-called fossil fuels. These fossil reservoirs – which can be thought of as another form of buried biomass – have normally been involved in the carbon cycle only on geological time-scales, but human intervention through the use of fossil fuels has radically changed this.

This discussion leads to an extremely important conclusion, crucial to all analyses of Earth and life:

The atmosphere itself is not a major reservoir of oxygen – it is merely a temporary transfer site for the gas as it is consumed or liberated by processes acting on other oxygen reservoirs.

2.4 Photosynthesis and the Earth's oxygen inventory

The atmospheric oxygen reservoir may be relatively small, but as is clear from Table 1.1, the atmospheric carbon dioxide reservoir is even smaller and so would be consumed by photosynthetic processes in a period that is very short by geological standards.

Photosynthesis is a marvellous process. Through the medium of chlorophyll in green plants, energy from sunlight brings about the combination of carbon dioxide from the atmosphere and water to form the stuff of life – biomass:

$$n\text{CO}_2 + n\text{H}_2\text{O} + \text{energy} \longrightarrow (\text{CH}_2\text{O})_n + n\text{O}_2 \qquad \text{(Equation 2.4)}$$

(in the atmosphere)   (biomass)   (in the atmosphere)

To some extent the term 'photosynthesis' has become synonymous with oxygen production. This is unfortunate, since there are photosynthetic processes that do *not* involve oxygen production. Strictly, when referring to the process described in Equation 2.4, we should speak of *oxygenic photosynthesis*. Oxygenic photosynthesis is a process that underpins much of the discussion in this book. It can be understood at many levels. At the simplest, it can be considered as the reverse of respiration, as shown by combining Equations 2.3 and 2.4:

$$n\text{CO}_2 + n\text{H}_2\text{O} + \text{energy} \underset{\text{respiration}}{\overset{\text{photosynthesis}}{\rightleftarrows}} (\text{CH}_2\text{O})_n + n\text{O}_2 \qquad \text{(Equation 2.5)}$$

(in the atmosphere)   (biomass)   (in the atmosphere)

Thinking in global terms, therefore, one has to ask: since the reaction that yields oxygen (photosynthesis) is balanced by a reaction that consumes oxygen (respiration), how could oxygen accumulate in the atmosphere, to the present level of 21% by volume? Also what stabilizes the amount of oxygen at this level? We shall be addressing these issues in subsequent chapters, but meanwhile a significant conclusion (which you have met before) can be drawn:

The amount of oxygen in the atmosphere today must be the result of differences between the rate at which oxygen is produced by (oxygenic) photosynthesis and the rate at which it is consumed by aerobic respiration, combustion and other processes.

Let us examine this conclusion more fully. Equation 2.4 shows that for every oxygen molecule generated and released during photosynthesis, one basic unit of biomass containing one atom of carbon is produced. Thus, if there are 1.2×10^{18} kg of molecular oxygen at large in the atmosphere today, the corresponding amount of biomass that must have been produced is 1.2×10^{18} kg $\times (30/32) = 1.1 \times 10^{18}$ kg. (Of course, as we saw in Section 1.2, the atmosphere is not the only reservoir of molecular oxygen – there are 7.8×10^{15} kg of molecular oxygen dissolved in the oceans, but this is rather insignificant in comparison to the amount in the atmosphere.)

The actual amount of *living* biomass is relatively tiny. There are only about 2×10^{15} kg of living biomass (Box 2.2) – approximately 0.002% (i.e. 1/500) of that needed to account for the present level of atmospheric oxygen.

■   What conclusion can you draw from this? Where is the 'missing' biomass?

■   It must have been somehow 'removed' from circulation.

In fact it is buried in the form of fossil organic matter in sediments. Sometimes this fossil material is easily identifiable, as in the form of peat, or as coal, oil and gas reserves, but much of it is obscure: finely dispersed carbonaceous matter in lake muds and elsewhere. This buried organic carbon plays a crucial role in the carbon cycle, but for now we can think of it as the buried result of the excess of photosynthesis over respiration.

It is important to appreciate that the oxygen in the atmosphere today is not the sum total of all the oxygen ever produced; nor is the buried biomass the accumulation of all that has ever been made. Both have been continuously recycled (Figure 2.1). This leads us to another crucial conclusion:

If the cyclical process involving photosynthesis and respiration had always been perfectly balanced, oxygen would never have accumulated in the atmosphere. It is only because geological processes cause the system to be one-sided, by burying biomass (organic carbon) in sediments, that the amount of oxygen in the atmosphere has been able to build up to 21%.

You can see from Equation 2.5, that if biomass were removed from the cycle (by burial), the level of O_2 in the atmosphere would increase as the biomass would no longer be available for respiration.

Is it just our good luck that organic carbon should be trapped in sediments? What would be the effect on the atmosphere of changing the amount of buried biomass? You should be in a position to answer these momentous questions for yourselves when you have finished studying this book.

2.5 Critical questions and a plan of campaign

These preliminary skirmishings with oxygen focus our attention on four key issues, which we shall explore from different angles in subsequent chapters:

♦   Has the oxygen level on Earth fluctuated in the geological past?

♦   What are the factors that have influenced the levels of atmospheric oxygen during the Earth's history?

♦   How and when did the atmospheric oxygen level attain its present level of 21%?

♦   How, if at all, is this level regulated?

There are no simple answers to these questions, and as so many factors are involved, investigating these issues can be somewhat complicated. So it is helpful to have a plan of how to proceed. In the following chapters, we shall examine the geological record for direct and indirect clues to oxygen levels and the processes controlling them. We first peer back through the abyss of time to locate various milestones denoting changes in the Earth's atmosphere (Chapters 3 and 4). With this frame of reference established, we shall then examine the processes responsible first for attaining and then stabilizing the atmospheric oxygen content. Finally, in Chapter 8, we shall examine a secondary – though still important issue – the role of ozone in the Earth's history, before we move on to consider another crucially important atmospheric gas, carbon dioxide, in Chapters 9 to 12.

2.6 Summary of Chapter 2

1 Biomass, which can be represented as $(CH_2O)_n$, and molecular oxygen are formed by photosynthesis from atmospheric carbon dioxide and water using sunlight.

2 Photosynthesis can be considered as the reverse of aerobic respiration.

3 During respiration, biomass is oxidized and carbon dioxide and energy are produced.

4 There are about 2×10^{15} kg of living biomass (i.e. 0.5–1×10^{15} kg of carbon) on land and about 7×10^{12} kg in the oceans (i.e. 2–4×10^{12} kg of carbon). Although the ocean biomass is small relative to that of the land, it is highly influential in the Earth System because of the short time-scales over which changes can take place in the oceans.

5 The residence time for oxygen in the atmosphere is short relative to the age of the Earth; thus the atmosphere itself is not a major reservoir for oxygen.

6 If the cyclical processes of photosynthesis and respiration had always been perfectly balanced, oxygen would never have accumulated in the atmosphere. It is only because geological processes cause the system to be one-sided, by burying biomass (i.e. organic carbon) in sediments, that the amount of oxygen in the atmosphere has been able to build up to its present level of 21%.

Now try the following questions to consolidate your understanding of Chapters 1 and 2.

Question 2.1
If the present-day atmosphere contains 0.036% carbon dioxide, what is the mass of carbon dioxide in the atmosphere in kilograms, and how does this compare with the mass of oxygen?

Question 2.2
Oceanographic studies show that about 1.2×10^{11} kg of organic carbon sinks down to the ocean floors to be buried in sediments. What is the annual contribution of oxygen to the atmosphere from this source, assuming that *all* of the carbon buried is of photosynthetic origin?

Question 2.3
Consider the amount of carbon dioxide in the Earth's atmosphere. Because it is so small, it could easily be entirely consumed via the photosynthetic processes of plant life. But this does not happen. Name *three* processes that limit the extent of plant life on Earth.

Chapter 3
The fossil record

3.1 Looking backwards through time

The Earth's geological record extends back almost
4 billion years (4 Ga), but it is frustratingly incomplete.
Nonetheless, it is to this flawed record that we must
turn for any analysis of global change. One obvious
problem is that there is no such thing as 'fossil' air to
provide a snapshot of the atmosphere billions of years
ago. Polar ice sheets contain bubbles of air but these
are only tens of thousands of years old. Analyses of
the gas in these bubbles have proved invaluable in
tracking atmospheric change in the relatively recent past, but the oldest glacier ice is
still juvenile compared with the age of the Earth. Amber, the gorgeous honey-brown
fossilized tree resin, also contains trapped air bubbles, along with perfectly
preserved insects (Figure 3.1); however, interactions between the resin and the
trapped air make it uncertain how representative this gas is of the contemporary
atmosphere that was trapped in the resin. Even if the air in amber has not been
modified, it would be of limited use as it would not be very old in geological terms –
the oldest amber is only about 70 million years old. (If you want to familiarize
yourself with geological time-scales, see Box 3.1.)

Figure 3.1
Bubbles of air are very
common in amber, along
with rarer fossils of insects
and still rarer fossil
amphibians. Attempts have
been made to study ancient
atmospheres from analysing
air bubbles in amber, but
unfortunately the trapped air
has been altered by reaction
with the enclosing resin. This
polished specimen is 6 cm in
length and 2 cm across.

Sherlock Holmes could deduce the occupation of his clients as soon as they stepped
into 221B Baker Street. He did not need to ask direct questions – he merely observed
indirect features, such as their posture or the colour of the mud on their shoes. As
we cannot obtain direct evidence about the early atmosphere, our quest, like Holmes',
must be for *indirect* clues to what the atmosphere was like in the past; we must look
for traces of things that had been exposed to the air.

Broadly speaking, we can draw on two sources of indirect evidence for the history
of the atmosphere:

◆   the fossil record of evolving life-forms;

◆   the rock record which preserves the effects of changes in oxygen levels on the
    weathering and deposition of sediments.

We shall discuss the rock record in Chapters 4 and 5, but for the moment we focus on
the evidence from the fossil record.

■   What sort of fossils would you look for in rocks that are 50 million years old
    if you wanted to demonstrate that the atmosphere then had a broadly similar
    oxygen level to that of today?

■   You would look for fossils of the same kind of animals as those alive today –
    e.g. mammals – that breathe air.

Mammals have dominated the Earth since the dinosaurs were extirpated about
65 million years ago. If we could travel backwards in time 65 million years, we
would, in fact, find the atmosphere much as we know it today. However, fossils of
mammals are not common because mammals have always been predominantly land-
dwellers, and fossil-bearing sediments are largely of marine origin. Other fossils, in
particular those of shellfish living in shallow water and dependent on dissolved
oxygen, are extremely abundant. Thus, the fossil record of the last 65 million years

Box 3.1 The geological time-scale and nomenclature

When 19th century geologists were first attempting to subdivide the Earth's history into meaningful units, they had no means of ascribing numerical ages to the units, so they employed a system of names to describe periods characterized by different fossil assemblages. Although radiometric dating has since provided absolute dates, the original nomenclature is still universally used, partly from custom, and partly because it provides a convenient shorthand, in much the same way as the period between 1837 and 1901 is generally described as the 'Victorian era'. Most of the names used are neologisms based on Greek words; many of them include the suffix – zoic, from the

Greek *zoion*, meaning animal. Spelling of some of the neologisms has varied over the years. For example, when Charles Lyell first defined the word 'paleontology' in the 1830s, he spelt it as we have here. Later in the 19th century and into the 20th century it was widely spelled with a diphthong – *palæontology*. More recently, the original spelling has been preferred. Given its historical precedence, we have followed this convention in this Course.

A vital milestone in the history of the Earth is set at 540 million years ago. Before that time, there is scant evidence in rocks for life on Earth, so the interval between 540 million years ago and the origin of the Earth (4.6 billion years ago) is called the Cryptozoic (hidden

life) Eon – it is also known as the Precambrian. More recently than 540 million years ago there is abundant fossil evidence for life, so the interval between the present and 540 million years ago is called the Phanerozoic (visible life) Eon.

The Cryptozoic Eon is divided into three Eras: the Hadean, which was essentially pre-biotic, the Archean (characterized by single-celled organisms) and the Proterozoic (characterized by the appearance of the first eukaryotes). These divisions are summarized on the Course Bookmark. (You should be aware that when looking at different sources it is not unusual to see slightly different dates attached to the various divisions on the geological time-scale.)

Because so many diverse fossils are found in the Phanerozoic record, this era has been more finely subdivided than the Cryptozoic. There are again three eras: the Paleozoic (ancient life), the Mesozoic (middle life), and the Cenozoic (recent life). Each of these is further divided into a number of shorter time intervals called Periods, such as the Carboniferous, the Cambrian and the Jurassic. Each Period is also subdivided again into successively finer epochs and ages, but you do not need to be concerned with these in this Course.

Although some of the names may be unfamiliar to you, you should try to remember them as they are widely used, and even creep into popular literature.

is one of an Earth teeming with life – life that was essentially similar to that present today.

Looking backwards beyond 65 million years ago becomes progressively more difficult because we enter less well-known territory, and our study of the record of the Earth's atmospheric oxygen content becomes inextricably interwoven with that of the evolution of life itself. We can only deal with some of the major milestones.

■ Can you suggest some stages in the evolution of life that may have a direct bearing on our investigation into the amount of atmospheric oxygen?

■ The key stages in evolution are the first appearance of air-breathing animals on dry land, the first appearance of green-leafed photosynthesizing plants on dry land and, most importantly, the first oxygenic photosynthetic organisms of *any* kind.

Before we can investigate what the fossil record for each of these stages can tell us about how the oxygen content has varied over time, we need to establish the 'units' we shall be using to quantify atmospheric oxygen levels.

There are two common ways of expressing the atmospheric oxygen level (or the level of any other atmospheric gas). We have already introduced one method in Chapter 1; this method gives the concentration as a proportion of the total atmosphere. Thus the concentration of oxygen in the present atmosphere is about 21% by volume. The second method expresses the oxygen level as a fraction of the present atmospheric level (PAL), and so it is given as a decimal in relation to today's oxygen level. Thus an oxygen content of 0.50 PAL is equivalent to an oxygen concentration of $0.50 \times 21\% = 10.5\%$ of the total atmosphere.

Activity 3.1

As the discussion in this chapter progresses, the inferred oxygen content of the atmosphere at various times in the geological past will be stated. As these values are given in the text, you should note them down.

We suggest you start by setting up a table with the column headings shown in Table 3.1. By the time you reach the end of this chapter you will have a summary table recording the changes in atmospheric oxygen level over geological time (as deduced from the fossil

Table 3.1 Table for Activity 3.1.

Age or age range	Atmospheric oxygen as a percentage of the total atmosphere	Atmospheric oxygen as a fraction of the present atmospheric level, PAL
present day	21%	1.0 PAL

record). We have shown the present-day value to start you off. Throughout the

chapter we shall remind you whenever you should enter a value in the table.

3.2 Interpreting the fossil record

3.2.1 The first land animals

Popular imagination focuses on dinosaurs, but little attention is paid to the animals that were around before the dinosaurs. Fossil evidence shows that the first life-forms to colonize the land were small wingless insects, mites, and spider-like animals. These were followed by the first fish-like amphibians, which crawled out of the oceans on to the land about 380 million years ago. These amphibians required oxygen to breathe, so we can be sure that by about 380 million years ago atmospheric oxygen was present, but it is more difficult to be certain how much oxygen there was. While the amphibians could perhaps have survived at an atmospheric oxygen level of 5–10% (0.25–0.5 PAL), it would be safer to say, in the absence of more substantial evidence, that the oxygen level 380 million years ago was broadly similar to that of the present day, because the ancestors of present-day amphibians probably required similar levels of oxygen to their descendants. (Add this value – for 380 million years to the present day – to your summary table in Activity 3.1.)

■   Could the first animals have colonized the lands before the first land plants came into existence?

■   No – whereas green plants can photosynthesize food directly from the atmosphere and soil, i.e. they are autotrophic, animals have to eat something – either plants or each other, i.e. they are heterotrophic.

3.2.2 The first land plants

Traces of the first recognizable land plants appear in the fossil record found in sediments that are about 460 million years old – these have been identified as simple mossy carpets that clung to rocks near water. (Similar, but more primitive algal colonies – algal mats – and bacteria may have been extensive in damp areas much earlier than this.)

Once plants became established, the 'greening of the land' seems to have taken place rapidly. In order to grow upwards, plants require a more solid structure than mosses have. About 400 million years ago, the oldest recognizable plants began to flourish. By 360 million years ago, extensive forests of trees with fern-like folliage existed. During the Carboniferous Period, 300 million years ago, the forests were so extensive, and the amount of biomass buried to form coal was so prodigious, that they were the source of the coal that eventually fuelled the Industrial Revolution. Many countries continue to depend on the fossil fuels that formed from carbon buried around 300 million years ago as their primary energy source.

Question 3.1

In the Carboniferous Period huge amounts of carbon were buried in the deposits which now form these primary energy reserves. What does this suggest to you about atmospheric oxygen levels during the time when the great coal swamps were being formed and buried?

Figure 3.2

These charcoal fragments on the weathered surface of a 300-million-year-old sedimentary rock from Donegal in Ireland, illustrate that charcoal became abundant in the rock record soon after the first forests became established. They also provide clear evidence for forest fires, and thus for atmospheric oxygen levels greater than about 12–15%.

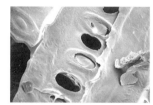

(a)

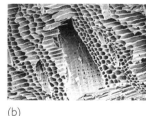

(b)

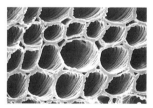

(c)

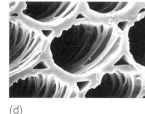

(d)

Figure 3.3

Microscopic sections of fossil charcoal demonstrate how the original cellular structure of wood is preserved after both fire and burial in sediments for hundreds of millions of years. Samples (a) and (b) are from the Jurassic Period and (c) and (d) are from the Carboniferous Period. Charcoal is very inert chemically and therefore an excellent candidate for fossilization.

Unambiguous fossil evidence for the existence of vast forests 360 million years ago indicates that oxygen production was under way on a large scale by then. It is difficult, however, to make quantitative estimates of how much of the oxygen that was generated accumulated in the atmosphere. Furthermore, widespread colonization of the land by plants would have had far-reaching environmental effects, e.g. the *albedo* or fraction of reflected solar energy on continental areas would have been much reduced, changing the global energy balance. Also, as a secondary effect, increased water loss from the plants could have led to increased atmospheric water vapour and hence to increased cloud cover, which would also have altered the Earth's albedo.

In the fossil record of the earliest forests of about 370 million years ago, one can find both an abundance of charcoal and evidence of the presence of large trees which were many metres high, comparable to modern trees (Figures 3.2 and 3.3). The distinguished American geochemist H. D. Holland of Harvard University has argued that the presence of charcoal in the fossil record provides unequivocal evidence of fires, possibly started by lightning strikes, raging through the forests. Laboratory experiments show that it is difficult to start a fire if the oxygen level is less than about 12–15% of the total atmosphere (0.6–0.7 PAL). On the other hand, at oxygen levels of about 30–35% (1.4–1.7 PAL), runaway, almost explosive combustion of forests, even green leaves, would take place, limiting the growth of vegetation to the most modest forms. Since there is conclusive evidence that both charcoal *and* mature trees were present in the great Carboniferous coal forests 300 million years ago, it follows that forest fires must have been sufficiently infrequent then to permit trees to grow to maturity. It is therefore reasonable to assume that the Earth's atmospheric oxygen content had reached somewhere between 15 and 30% of the total atmosphere (0.7–1.4 PAL) by about 300 million years ago, i.e. fires could have started but they would also have burnt themselves out.

Thus, the land plant fossil record enables us to deduce that back as far as about 400 million years ago, atmospheric oxygen levels were similar to those of today, with a range of between 15 and 30% oxygen content at about 300 million years ago. (Add this information to your summary table.) Before 460 million years, the record is rather murky: bacterial life may have been widespread on land, but it has left few traces – the continents were barren expanses of rock, gravel and sand, possibly covered with algal mats in moist areas.

▦ Does the absence of any land plants before about 460 million years ago mean that photosynthesis was not taking place?

▦ No – photosynthesis can take place wherever organisms can use chlorophyll to utilize the energy of sunlight for food production, especially in shallow water and areas of wet ground.

Nonetheless, colonization of the land by plants would have represented such a vast increase in the potential for photosynthesis that it seems inevitable that the atmosphere would have undergone a significant long-term change at this time. Recall that today there is several hundred times as much living biomass on land as there is in the oceans.

While the absolute amounts of land and marine biomass are clearly important in considerations of the role of oxygen in atmospheric evolution, there is another important determinant.

▦ Can you recall what it is?

▦ It is the rate at which carbon is being removed from the system and buried – buried organic carbon does not take part in combustion, respiration or oxidation.

Other things being equal, it is only the *imbalance* between photosynthesis and respiration caused by the burial of organic carbon that leads to accumulation of oxygen in the atmosphere. The rate at which organic carbon burial takes place depends on a complex range of geological factors, but it seems probable that the evolution of land forests, capable of giving rise to extensive deltaic coal swamps, also affected the global rate of organic carbon burial. An important factor to consider when trying to quantify this burial rate is the relative rates of burial of land and marine biomass. Although there is less living marine than land biomass at any one time, marine biomass and its organic carbon may be more efficiently buried than land biomass.

▦ Why should this be?

▦ Land biomass – such as forest timber and leaves – is more likely to be rotted at the surface of the Earth than marine biomass, which dies and sinks to the bottom of the oceans.

A further complicating factor is that a large proportion of undecayed land biomass may be transported by rivers into the marine environment, to be deposited below sea level in accumulating piles of deltaic sediments like those of the modern Mississippi.

3.2.3 The earliest animals and algae

The first fish-like amphibians crawled out of the oceans about 380 million years ago (Section 3.2.1), but what life-forms were present in the oceans before that time? And what does the available fossil evidence indicate about the atmospheric oxygen levels at the time? (Remember we are able to deduce atmospheric oxygen levels from marine evidence because molecular oxygen is soluble in water.)

Prokaryotes, you may recall, are simple cells lacking nuclei; eukaryotes possess a nucleus which encapsulates much of the cell's genetic material. Ultimately, this more complex cellular structure led to the rich evolutionary possibilities inherent in sexual reproduction, and to the diversity of modern life. Although the continents were barren prior to 400 million years ago, the oceans were teeming with life. There was an abundance of complex animals, such as a trilobites, and a wealth of simpler organisms. This abundance of life can be readily traced back through successively older rocks in the fossil record until about 540 million years ago. Beyond this point, the fossil record abruptly becomes sparse. There are indeed older fossils, but they are few and far between. The great explosion of life that took place within the oceans about 540 million years ago is one of the most important milestones in the history of the Earth, but it is also one of the most difficult to interpret. For now, we should merely note that the fossil record suggests that between 540 and 400 million years ago, the oceans contained prolific animal life, which presumably was sustained by dissolved oxygen.

Figure 3.4
A typical fossil from the 580-million-year-old Ediacaran fauna of South Australia. This fossil, *Medusina mawsoni*, is a few centimetres across, and probably resembled a modern jellyfish.

Another milestone took place at about 580 million years ago, when there was another spectacular burst in animal evolution. This is best manifested in a remarkable assemblage of fossils from the Ediacara hills 600 km north of Adelaide in South Australia. A sandy layer in these rocks contains an assemblage of fossils (known as the Ediacaran fossils), that were derived from recognizably soft-bodied animals, resembling those that one might encounter washed up anonymously on a beach today – jellyfish, segmented worms, and so on. None had shells or hard parts, but this faunal assemblage marks the very first known appearance of animals in the fossil record (Figure 3.4).

At one time, it was widely believed that the Ediacaran explosion itself signified a major change in the atmospheric oxygen level – an increase that permitted the sudden evolution of large animals to take place. This view is now seen to be too simplistic. The animals in the Ediacaran fauna were so advanced in evolutionary terms that they must have descended from a line of simpler ancestors. A 'guesstimate' of the atmospheric oxygen level indicated by the Ediacaran fauna is about 1–2% (0.05–0.1 PAL). (Add this value to your summary table, Activity 3.1.)

An even more important milestone, however, was when the oxygen level first exceeded the 0.2% (0.01 PAL) threshold, since most biologists agree that 0.2% atmospheric oxygen is the bare minimum required for the simplest eukaryote cells to metabolize. Although most of the Edicaran animals were only a few centimetres long, some were quite large (up to 1 m in length), with complex body structures. Their ancestors must have been much smaller and simpler. Thus we can conclude that when eukaryotes first evolved, atmospheric oxygen levels must have already reached 0.2%. But when did eukaryotes first appear?

The earliest eukaryotes were *extremely* simple, many of them being unicellular amoebas and algae. Unfortunately, these microscopic blobs of goo did not leave easily recognizable fossils. Furthermore, it is understandably difficult to distinguish between prokaryotic and eukaryotic cell forms in such early fossils as have been found.

Nevertheless, paleontologists have been able to unearth a few critical facts: fossils found in rocks from Spitsbergen, an island off Arctic Norway, show that eukaryotes were abundant and diverse between 1000 and 580 million years ago. The oldest suspected fossil eukaryote of all has been found in rocks 2.1 billion years old from Michigan, USA. It was a primitive organism, found in the form of spirally coiled filaments about 1 mm wide and up to 90 mm long, known as *Grypania*. Although *Grypania* probably was a eukaryote, some doubt remains. During 1995, paleontologists discovered well-preserved, 1700-million-year-old fossils of seaweed-like algal plants several centimetres long in China. It is possible to deduce from the size and structure of *Grypania* and the Chinese algae that they probably needed at least 0.2% atmospheric oxygen to survive. Thus, you can record in your summary table that oxygen reached at least 0.2% by 2.1 billion years ago.

3.2.4 The first photosynthesizers

Although microscopic in size, the enormous number of planktonic photosynthesizing organisms in the modern oceans mean that their role in oxygen production is significant. A single algal cell may be only 10^{-5} m ($10\,\mu m$) in diameter, but during algal 'blooms' there may be as many as 10^8 individual cells in a litre of seawater. Although some modern planktonic organisms manufacture tiny but elegant shells for themselves (Figure 2.4), which can be preserved in the fossil record, their ancient predecessors did not. However, there are grounds for believing that large numbers of simple photosynthetic organisms flourished before the first obvious, fossilizable animals appeared in the fossil record 540 million years ago. The most convincing evidence for the existence of early photosynthetic organisms is provided by fossilized stromatolites. (Stromatolites were discussed in *Origins of Earth and Life*, but some general points about them are summarized in Box 3.2.)

Box 3.2 Stromatolites – a review

Fossil stromatolites are not actually 'fossils' of individual animals, in the usual sense like the trilobites sought by collectors, but they are distinctive accumulations of calcium carbonate ($CaCO_3$). Because calcium carbonate is barely soluble in water, and because the masses of rocky material involved are so large, stromatolites survive all manner of geological upheavals.

Prokaryotic cyanobacteria, or blue–green algae, were among the earliest photosynthetic organism. Some cyanobacteria did not drift freely around the oceans as plankton, but lived in complex associations in warm, shallow waters forming sheet-like layers at the surface of sandy or muddy sediments, which were bound together with sticky, filamentous outgrowths to form resistant mats (Figure 3.5). The cyanobacteria used sunlight for photosynthesis in the same way as modern plants, and they also extracted calcium carbonate from seawater and deposited it within their surface mats. Others secreted calcium carbonate as part of their metabolism, or were gelatinous and trapped fine sediments. Successive layers of calcium carbonate accumulated through time, so the final resulting stromatolite often resembles a stack of pancakes. Others resemble lumpy, potato-shaped masses; still others are irregular, cabbage-shaped masses, but all show a characteristic internally layered structure (Figure 3.6).

Figure 3.5
Filamentous living algal mats bind together the uppermost layer of sediments and evaporites in this hot low-lying coastal plain in Oman, forming a monotonous expanse that superficially looks devoid of life.

Figure 3.6
Cross-section through a typical stromatolite, showing the diagnostic layered structure. The modern stromatolites in Figure 3.7 would probably look similar if cut through. The fossil examples are exposed in 2.7-billion-year-old rocks at Belingwe, Zimbabwe.

The oldest stromatolites are found in rocks in the 3.5-billion-year-old Warrawoona Group from northwestern Australia, but stromatolites are also abundant in 2.5-billion-year-old sediments deposited in South Africa. Inevitably, many of the oldest stromatolites are poorly preserved and therefore of equivocal origin, but examples from the 2.8-billion-year-old Fortescue Group of Western Australia are so well preserved that tapering filaments of the original bacterial material can still be identified microscopically.

Perhaps surprisingly, we can be fairly confident about how the organisms that gave rise to these stromatolites lived and metabolized because some stromatolite-producing organisms still exist, for example, in warm, shallow brackish water at Shark Bay, eastern Australia, where they form stromatolites that take the form of small reefs which are intermittently exposed by the tides (Figure 3.7).

Since these modern stromatolites are made by colonies of oxygenic-photosynthesizing cyanobacteria, it is not unreasonable to suppose that the presence of stromatolites in the fossil record suggest that photosynthesis was taking place at least as far back as 3.5 billion years ago.

A note of caution should be introduced here. Although the cyanobacteria that construct modern stromatolites are indeed oxygenic photosynthesizers, we cannot be absolutely certain that the earliest organisms that constructed stromatolites were all *oxygenic* photosynthesizers. Like some anaerobic bacteria, their metabolism may not have involved free oxygen at all. So, while the existence of stromatolites in ancient rocks is strong circumstantial evidence that oxygen was being manufactured, it is much more difficult to quantify the *amount* of oxygen entering the atmosphere. For that, we must look at the rocks themselves (Chapter 4).

Figure 3.7
Modern stromatolites at Shark Bay, eastern Australia.

3.3 Photosynthesis and the carbon isotopic record

The idea that simple (photosynthetic) life-forms were prolific on the early Earth is crucial to our story. Although fossil stromatolites provide some clues, further confirmation is needed. Carbon isotopes provide good evidence.

Photosynthesis is a complex process, but we can think of it as occurring in two stages: in the first stage, carbon dioxide from the atmosphere is 'imported' into the cell; in the second stage, an enzyme known as ribulose bisphosphate carboxylase/oxygenase (which is abbreviated to **Rubisco**) is involved in forming biomass $(CH_2O)_n$ from the imported CO_2.

In both of these stages, there is a fractionation of the isotope ^{12}C from ^{13}C, with the lighter ^{12}C being concentrated preferentially in the cell, relative to the heavier ^{13}C. As you have seen elsewhere in the Course, these variations in isotope concentration can be expressed in terms of $\delta^{13}C$ notation, where $\delta^{13}C$ denotes the ratio (and hence the fractionation) of ^{13}C relative to ^{12}C:

$$\delta^{13}C = \left[\frac{\left(^{13}C/^{12}C\right)\text{ sample}}{\left(^{13}C/^{12}C\right)\text{ standard}} - 1 \right] \times 1000\,(\text{‰}) \qquad \text{(Equation 3.1)}$$

The $\delta^{13}C$ values are given as parts per thousand, or per mil (‰). If you need to remind yourself how $\delta^{13}C$ values are interpreted, look back to *Origins of Earth and Life*.

Measurement of the carbon isotope ratios in ancient sedimentary rocks can tell us something about the amount of photosynthesis that took place in the early Earth. The buried carbon is of two types, as you may recall:

◆   **Organic carbon** (C_{org}), the *reduced* form, which can be thought of as the 'fossil' residue of biological substances, and is produced by biological processes. Organic carbon residues have no fixed chemical composition, but generally contain carbon combined with hydrogen and other elements. Most occurs in the form of **kerogen**, the resistant end product of organic debris derived from organisms and the products of their metabolism.

◆   **Carbonate carbon** (C_{carb}), the *oxidized* form, which can be produced by both biological processes, as in formation of shells, and by non-biological processes, as when stalactites form from dripping water in caves.

Fortunately for us, the carbon isotope ratios in the C_{org} and C_{carb} reservoirs are not obliterated by the heat and pressure involved in burial, although some degradation of the sediments does occur. The variations in $\delta^{13}C$ in the C_{org} and C_{carb} reservoirs throughout the history of the Earth and the range of values in recent sediments and living organisms are shown in Figure 3.8. This is one of the most interesting diagrams in the whole rich history of Earth and life; it is known as the **Schidlowski diagram**, after its creator, Manfred Schidlowski.

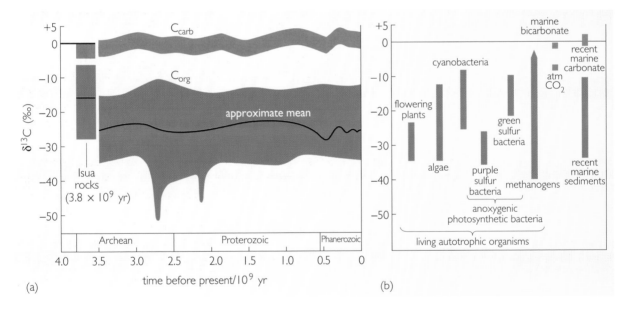

One complication in interpreting this diagram is that the $\delta^{13}C_{org}$ values used in Figure 3.8 have been slightly perturbed by post-depositional thermal degradation of kerogen, which results in preferential loss of ^{13}C-depleted, hydrogen-rich products. (If ^{13}C depleted material is removed, the $^{13}C/^{12}C$ ratio of the remaining sample would be higher, and so the $\delta^{13}C$ value would rise.) This loss can be corrected if the H : C ratio of the material is known. A modified Schidlowksi diagram such as Figure 3.9, for the Proterozoic Period, can then be constructed.

◼   How does Figure 3.9 differ from the unmodified Schidlowksi diagram, Figure 3.8?

◼   There is still a consistent difference between $\delta^{13}C$ for the C_{carb} and C_{org} reservoirs, but there is more variation and a general tendency for $\delta^{13}C_{org}$ values to be lower in the Archean (−44‰) than in the Proterozoic (−34‰).

Figure 3.8
The Schidlowski diagram. (a) The $\delta^{13}C$ values for the organic carbon (C_{org}) and carbonate carbon (C_{carb}) reservoirs over 3.8 million years of the Earth's history. (b) The range of values found in recent marine sediments and modern autotrophic organisms.

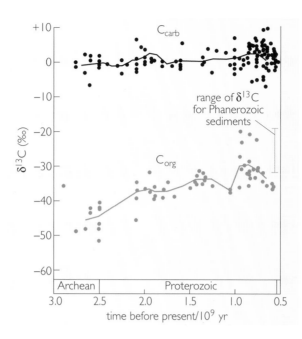

Figure 3.9
A modified version of the Schidlowski diagram, showing variations in $\delta^{13}C$ for organic carbon (C_{org}) and carbonate carbon (C_{carb}) through time, adjusted for the effects of changes caused by burial and heating.

The Schidlowski diagram shows that the isotopic composition of organic carbon has fluctuated somewhat over time, but has retained its distinctly different signature from carbonate carbon, which has varied only slightly in isotopic composition over time. Remarkably, the *difference* between $\delta^{13}C$ in the C_{org} reservoir and the C_{carb} reservoir shows only relatively minor variation over 3.8 billion years, despite the fact that both reservoirs have been constantly turned over by geological and biological processes. It is not so surprising that $\delta^{13}C$ in the C_{carb} reservoir has remained at or near zero, since this reservoir is much bigger than the C_{org} reservoir – about five times larger.

Most modern oxygenic photosynthetic micro-organisms and green plants utilize a photosynthetic pathway in which biomass in the form of a three-carbon compound (a phosphoglycerate) is produced from atmospheric carbon dioxide. Higher plants that rely on this mechanism exclusively are termed C3 plants to acknowledge the significance of the three-carbon group. Some more modern plant groups employ different pathways and are therefore termed C4 plants – this is, however, a more recent development in plant evolution, i.e. over the last 14 million years.

The fact that the mean $\delta^{13}C$ in the C_{org} reservoir has remained at values close to that found in today's organisms for about 3.5 billion years, suggests that photosynthesis (specifically via the C3 pathway involving the isotope-discriminating properties of Rubisco), has probably been active since the earliest history of the Earth.

Therefore this isotopic data supports the suggestion we made from the stromatolite record that oxygenic photosynthesis has been taking place for the past 3.5 billion years – the evidence from these 'chemical fossils' stretches further back than the visible fossil record. Note that all the available evidence suggests that the *very first* life-forms on Earth did not use oxygen in their metabolism, and they may not even have been photosynthesizers. Anoxygenic photosynthesizers most probably evolved before oxygenic photosynthesizers, but it is not possible to determine from the available fossil (stromatolite) or isotopic evidence when the first oxygenic photosynthesizers evolved: the oldest fossil evidence does not permit distinction between oxygenic and anoxygenic forms. However, since anoxygenic photosynthesizers had no effect on atmospheric oxygen levels (by definition) we do not need to explore this controversy.

3.4 How much life? – quantifying the fossil record

Stromatolites in ancient rocks are good evidence of early life. But they are not common – most ancient rocks contain no visible trace of life at all. How then can one estimate the *amounts* of biomass in the early Earth and therefore the amount of oxygen being produced?

One way is to investigate how the amount of C_{org} in sediments has varied through geological time. Modern sediments contain on average between 0.5 and 0.6% C_{org}, mostly in the form of kerogen. (An intermediate product in the breakdown of organic material in rocks is *petroleum*. If the organic material is dispersed through sediments, oil-shales may result. Fuels can be extracted from the oil-shales by destructive distillation of the kerogens contained in them.)

Figure 3.10 shows that the proportion of C_{org} in the sediments has oscillated around a mean of about 0.5% throughout the whole of geological time. Even some of the earliest known sediments, the 3.8-billion-year-old rocks from Isua, western Greenland, contain about 0.6% C_{org}!

The fact that the C_{org} content has been fairly constant over almost 4 billion years, indicates that shortly after life originated on the early Earth, it must have become prodigiously active, generating amounts of biomass (and therefore oxygen) comparable to those that exist today. This initially astounding conclusion becomes less surprising when one considers that simple microbial communities have always been among the biosphere's most productive ecosystems. Prokaryotes are capable of enormous rates of primary productivity: they can turn atmospheric carbon dioxide into biomass at staggering rates, at around $0.01\,kg\,C_{org}\,m^{-2}\,day^{-1}$. If these rates of primary production by simple photosynthesizing prokaryotes were true of ancient prokaryotes, the global rate of production of biomass (and hence C_{org} burial) probably did not vary greatly during subsequent evolution.

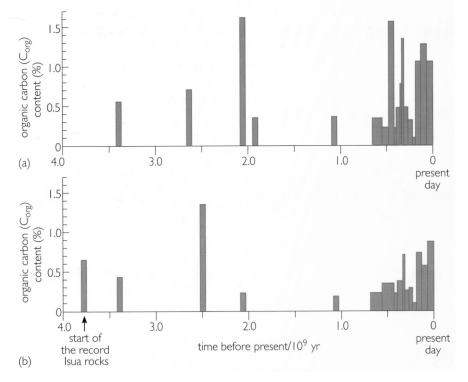

Figure 3.10
The organic carbon (C_{org}) content of (a) shales and (b) average sediments through geological time. Note that the data are very incomplete, but that the range of values for ancient rocks are not markedly different from those of younger rocks. The start of the record is represented by the Isua rocks.

This is a thought-provoking conclusion, and it needs some examination. We stated in Chapter 2 that the amount of oxygen in the air today reflects the balance between photosynthesis and respiration, and that oxygen can only accumulate in the atmosphere if organic carbon is removed from the system by burial in sediments. Although we know the *proportion* of C_{org} in sediments, we do not know much about the actual *size* (mass) of the sediment reservoirs in the early Earth, but they were probably smaller than today, because the continents were smaller. But even if the total mass of the C_{org} reservoir in sediments has increased through time, the steady *proportion* of C_{org} in sediments nonetheless implies that at any time relatively large amounts of oxygen were being produced.

▨   If oxygen was being produced by photosynthesis and organic carbon was being buried in sediments in the early Earth at rates broadly comparable to those today, but the level of atmospheric oxygen was much lower than that found today, what conclusion *must* follow?

▨   Some other process must have been consuming photosynthetic oxygen.

We return to this crucial issue in Chapters 4 and 5.

3.5 Summary of Chapter 3

1   Examination of the fossil record enables us to deduce past atmospheric oxygen levels.

2   Mammals have been abundant for the last 65 million years, so the atmosphere was probably similar then to that found today.

3   Amphibians first came ashore some 380 million years ago – they probably needed a minimum atmospheric oxygen level of between 5 and 10%.

4   Land plants evolved about 460 million years ago, and led to a rapid 'greening of the land'. Evidence for both charcoal (indicating fire) and mature trees in the early forests shows that atmospheric oxygen levels were probably between 15 and 30% by about 300 million years ago.

5   Shelly fossils first appeared in the fossil record 540 million years ago, but the first eukaryote fossils are much older, at least 1.7 billion years old. Eukaryotes are thought to need atmospheric oxygen levels of at least 0.2% (0.01 PAL) to metabolize.

6   Photosynthesizing organisms (e.g. some cyanobacteria) are even more ancient, appearing about 3.6 billion years ago.

7   The Schidlowski diagram compares the carbon isotope signature ($\delta^{13}C$) in the C_{carb} and C_{org} reservoirs through geological time. Because the two reservoirs show a consistent difference in $\delta^{13}C$ over the last 3.5 billion years, it is likely that photosynthesis via the C3 pathway, has been operating throughout that time.

8   Photosynthesizing prokaryotes are capable of prodigious rates of primary productivity. Thus, even in the most ancient sediments, the amount of buried organic carbon (C_{org}) is similar to that in modern sediments, about 0.5–0.6%.

Now try the following questions to consolidate your understanding of this chapter.

Question 3.2

If the total amount of living biomass on Earth were to increase, would this be manifested in the $\delta^{13}C$ signature of the C_{carb} and C_{org} reservoirs?

Question 3.3

The rapid 'greening of the land' following the evolution of land plants intuitively suggests a major change in the atmosphere, and particularly an increase in its oxygen content. Why should one be cautious about accepting this intuitively convincing conclusion at face value?

Question 3.4

There were no predators around in the early Earth which could graze on the prolific photosynthesizing organisms. If there had been, would this have limited the total amount of living biomass?

Chapter 4
The rock record

4.1 Introduction

At the end of Chapter 3 we concluded that there must have been 'some other process' on the early Earth that consumed some of the oxygen that was being produced by the life-forms present at the time, preventing it from accumulating in the atmosphere.

As you may recall from Chapter 2, oxygen reacts readily with iron to produce iron oxides. More importantly in terms of our present investigation, oxygen reacts in a similar way with a proportion of the constituents of rocks, oxidizing some of the metal atoms in their molecules. Such oxidation reactions are often referred to as *inorganic* oxidations because they involve inorganic compounds, so distinguishing them from organic oxidations which involve organic carbon compounds. Significantly, these inorganic processes use up some of the oxygen produced by life-forms; they also mean that rocks contain a record of the atmosphere's oxidizing ability which directly reflects the amount of oxygen present in the atmosphere. So, by examining various types of rock it is possible to glean evidence about the oxygen levels as far back as 4 billion years ago. We shall look, in particular, at the oxides of iron (Section 4.2) which are present in red beds, banded iron formations and paleosols, before turning our attention to another oxygen indicator – the oxide of uranium which occurs in uranium minerals (Section 4.3).

Information about even earlier oxygen levels can be obtained by going deeper into the Earth and considering how the oxidation state of the mantle has changed over the Earth's history (Section 4.4). Going further back in time to consider the Earth in its earliest days (Section 4.5) is less fruitful but raises some interesting questions. What picture, then, can be built up of the evolution of the Earth's early atmosphere from all this evidence? Several investigators have developed models of this evolution. In Section 4.6, we look at one of these which neatly draws together the facts to form a credible picture, which will be developed in more detail in later chapters.

4.2 Evidence from iron-bearing deposits

4.2.1 Characteristics of iron in the rock record

Iron pyrites, which is often referred to as just 'pyrite' or 'fools' gold', is a common mineral that occurs mostly in tiny crystals dispersed through sediments, but it is also often sold in the form of brassy cubes as an ornament. Pyrite is a compound of iron and sulfur, FeS_2, with iron present in the reduced form, i.e. the ferrous form, $Fe(II)$. (If you need a reminder about some of the properties of iron, see Box 4.1.) When sealed within a rock deep in the Earth, pyrite is stable, but when exposed to even small amounts of air in a warm, humid environment, it oxidizes rapidly undergoing a series of reactions which can be represented as follows:

$$\underset{\text{pyrite}}{4FeS_2} + \underset{\substack{\text{humid} \\ \text{atmosphere}}}{15O_2 + 8H_2O} \longrightarrow \underset{\text{haematite}}{2Fe_2O_3} + \underset{\substack{\text{sulfuric} \\ \text{acid}}}{8H_2SO_4} \qquad \text{(Equation 4.1)}$$

Other examples of red beds include the 'Old Red' Sandstones of Scotland, which were deposited about 380 million years ago. Several natural landmarks such as Orkney's great sea stack called the Old Man of Hoy are composed of these splendid rocks, which were made famous in the 19th century by Hugh Miller, the Victorian equivalent of David Attenborough. Although Old Red Sandstones are known to have been deposited in huge inland basins, and therefore are clearly non-marine in origin, they are particularly well-known for discoveries of beautifully preserved fish fossils. These fish lived and died in shallow inland seas or lakes of a type similar to the Aral Sea, which has largely dried up over the last 30 years.

Amongst the magnificent mountains of the western Highlands of Scotland is another group of red beds, known as the Torridonian sandstones, which were laid down under similar conditions to the Old Red Sandstones. Although almost identical to the Old Red Sandstones, they differ in one respect: they lack any form of visible fossils. They were deposited about a *billion* years ago; long before fish or other complex animals had evolved.

Fossiliferous or not, red beds in Britain show that there was an oxidizing atmosphere sufficient to convert ferrous iron into haematite, i.e. ferric oxide, at least as far back as 1 billion years ago, although the exact amount of oxygen present is more difficult to determine.

Britain is not alone in possessing red beds. About 250 million years ago huge deserts covered the heart of the enormous ancient continent known as Pangea, leading to the deposition of red beds which are now found worldwide – the red beds of the Vale of Eden are only an outpost of those deposits. Many other red beds are known in older rocks. Several different horizons of red beds are exposed in the 1.6 km high walls of the Grand Canyon in Arizona (Figure 4.4). The rocks at the bottom of the Grand Canyon are 1.2 billion years older than those at the top. Although not the most prominent of the cliff-forming units seen in the Canyon, one of the oldest sedimentary formations there is a red bed about 1 billion years old. Still older red beds turn up in the Huronian formations of Ontario, Canada; these are about 2 billion years old.

There are no red beds older than 2 billion years. This is highly significant. We saw in Chapter 3 that there was evidence that oxygen was present, albeit at a low level, as far back as 2 billion years ago. Formation of red beds requires oxygen, so their arrival in the rock

Figure 4.2
The red desert sands of the Rubh al Kahli, one of the great dune fields of the world, dominate this spacecraft view of the Red Sea and Gulf of Aden. These were deposited in recent geological times. Similar environments can be inferred in ancient rocks containing 'fossil' dunes, such as those shown in Figure 4.3.

Figure 4.3
Dune bedding is evident in the 200-million-year-old Navajo sandstone of Zion National Park, Utah.

Figure 4.4
Red sandstones of the 300-million-year-old Supai formation dominate this view of the Grand Canyon, Arizona.

record 2 billion years ago, and their absence in older rocks, provides evidence that the Earth's atmosphere became definitely oxidizing about 2 billion years ago.

However, it would be premature to conclude that the absence of red beds in rocks older than 2 billion years indicates that there was *no* oxygen at all in the atmosphere. It just means that there can, at best, have been only a trace – insufficient to oxidize the iron minerals at the surface of the Earth.

■   Would it be correct to conclude that the appearance of red beds in the rock record of 2 billion years ago marked the first evolution of oxygenic photosynthetic organisms?

■   No: while it is a tempting conclusion to draw, it is not correct – there is evidence of much older oxygenic photosynthesizers in the form of stromatolites.

Clearly, something important happened about 2 billion years ago. We shall explore that further in Chapter 5.

4.2.3 Banded iron formations

Characteristics of banded iron formations
When we look back through time, into the aeons before red beds were deposited, we find in the rock record widespread examples of an enigmatic rock type that has profound implications for the history of atmospheric oxygen – and for industrial civilization. These rocks are the so-called **banded iron formations** (**BIFs**). They are by far the world's most important commercial sources of iron – 90% of the iron mined globally is extracted from BIFs. Without BIFs, our modern world would be a very different place.

Figure 4.5
Mount Tom Price iron ore mine, Hamersley Ranges, Western Australia.

BIFs are amongst the oldest known rocks on Earth – those of the Isua group in Western Greenland are 3.8 billion years old. They occur throughout the world: one particularly important BIF deposit is in the Hamersley Ranges in Western Australia. It is several hundred metres thick and occupies a basin more than 300 km in diameter – large enough to supply much of the iron for the Japanese car industry. While the size of BIFs deposits such as at Hamersley is awesome (Figure 4.5), their fine structure is perplexing.

Banded iron formations are exactly what their name implies: they are rock formations that are characterized by finely banded dark brown, iron-rich layers alternating with lighter-coloured, iron-poor layers. These iron-rich bands contain the highly insoluble iron oxides: haematite (Fe_2O_3), limonite ($Fe_2O_3.3H_2O$) and magnetite (Fe_3O_4). Chert, a flinty rock composed of precipitated silica, dominates the iron-poor bands. Generally, the layers in BIFs are about a centimetre or so thick with sub-millimetre size microbanding, but larger-scale rhythmic banding is found in some deposits (Figure 4.6). Individual microbands, sometimes only millimetres thick, can often extend for tens of kilometres. How could such

The first hypothesis is now less favoured, because there is particularly compelling evidence drawn from oceanographic studies in suppost of the latter scenario, so we shall now review this.

The sheer scale of BIF deposits is such that ocean basins are almost certainly implicated. (Some estimates of the rate of BIF deposition in the Hamersley basin are as high as $10^9\,kg\,yr^{-1}$; that is about a million tonnes per year of iron oxide). Now, one of the most exciting oceanographic discoveries of the last decade was that of **'black smokers'** – plumes of hot, mineral-rich fluids which spew out of cracks and fissures along mid-ocean ridges (Figure 4.7). In places, these **hydrothermal vents** are the homes of colonies of bizarre creatures (as we have seen elsewhere in the Course), whose entire ecology is built around these deep-ocean sources of energy and minerals. These vents are relevant to our present discussion because analyses of the trace element chemistry of modern deep-ocean hydrothermal deposits show a close correlation with similar analyses carried out on ancient BIFs. The minerals escaping from the modern hydrothermal vents come directly from the Earth's mantle, which underlies the vents at a depth of only a few kilometres. As vast 'black smokers' probably gushed beneath the oceans of the early Earth, it therefore seems highly likely that the iron deposited in BIFs was derived originally from the mantle. Although *some* of the iron in BIFs might possibly have been derived from continental sediments, only the mantle could plausibly have provided a sufficiently large source.

Figure 4.7
Modern mid-ocean ridge black smoker. Heated seawater, at about 350 °C, emerges from the sea bed and on contact with cold water precipitates metal sulfides, building the vent chimney and forming the dense plume of black 'smoke'. The field of view is about 1–2 m across.

The process that might have been involved in the formation of BIFs is illustrated in Figure 4.8. As seawater flowed through the cracks and fissures in the upper oceanic crust, it dissolved minerals and injected them into the deep oceans in their reduced form through the hydrothermal vents via hydrothermal activity. It is widely accepted that iron originating from hydrothermal vents on mid-ocean ridges on the early Earth entered an oxygen-deficient or anoxic environment, different from that of modern black smokers: the iron thus escaped precipitation at the vents themselves, and was deposited in much shallower, oxygenated water on continental margins.

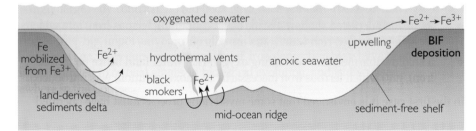

Figure 4.8
A schematic diagram illustrating the origin of BIFs. Some of the soluble iron present in the anoxic seawater could also have been derived from the slopes of continental shelves that were covered with sediments, but this was probably a negligible source compared to that supplied by hydrothermal vents linked directly to the mantle.

How did the iron get from the mid-ocean ridge vents to shallow water, crossing large expanses of oceans in so doing? One idea is that the iron was actually consumed by bacterial organisms which flourished near the vents, and that these then drifted away in vast colonies like modern plankton 'blooms'. When a floating bacterial 'bloom' entered shallow (oxygenated) water, mass mortality would have led to the deposition of a thin film of iron-rich organic material. After a while, the organic material would have been recycled, but the iron would have been left in its highly insoluble oxide form.

Hydrothermal vents provide satisfactorily sources for the enormous quantities of iron involved in the formation of BIFs, but what of the large amounts of oxygen required in order to deposit BIFs in marine basins?

■   What do you think would have been the most plausible source of the oxygen needed in the water to precipitate the iron?

■   Oxygenic photosynthesizing organisms are likely candidates.

We saw in Chapter 3 that stromatolites have existed on the Earth for about 3 billion years, and there is strong evidence to suppose that cyanobacteria were alive in shallow waters and generating oxygen while the BIFs were being deposited. Although photosynthetic activity could have produced quite a strongly oxidizing environment locally – in a confined basin, for example – it would not necessarily have produced a strongly oxidizing atmosphere.

Question 4.2
If a single iron-rich layer 1 mm thick consisting of pure haematite extends over a circular basin 200 km in diameter, how much oxygen would have been required to form it by oxidation of ferrous iron? Using the data on photosynthesis and biomass given in Section 2.4, calculate how much biomass would have been formed when this amount of oxygen was released during photosynthesis. How does this figure compare with the amount of modern marine biomass? (The density of haematite is $5.5 \times 10^3 \, \text{kg m}^{-3}$.)

Figure 4.9
Varved sands, deposited during the last great glaciation, from Saksmaki, Finland. Numerous small fault movements have later disrupted the regular laminations.

Banding in BIFs
We still have to explain the millions of alternations of reducing and oxidizing conditions represented by the fine layering of the iron-rich oxides and iron-poor cherts that defined BIFs.

No one really has a convincing explanation of this, but there are some indications of a possible process. The very fine scale of the laminations seen in BIFs closely resembles that in the layers of sediment known as **varves**, which are deposited in lakes in glacial regions today. In winter, when everything is frozen, only a thin layer of extremely fine-grained materials is deposited; in the spring thaw, much more material is deposited (Figure 4.9). So, the layers in BIFs may be evidence of a similar sort of seasonal process, with the banding reflecting annual changes brought about by melting of glacial ice, or perhaps monthly changes, like tidal variations.

As you can see from Equation 4.3, during the first stage of weathering, Fe^{2+} ions are liberated in solution, along with bicarbonate ions, (HCO_3^-). Other elements in the rocks, such a sodium also liberate soluble ions. If there is any dissolved oxygen around, the Fe^{2+} ions will be immediately precipitated in the form of insoluble Fe^{3+} ions:

$$4\,Fe^{2+} + O_2 + 8HCO_3^- + 4H_2O \longrightarrow 2Fe_2O_3 + 8H_2CO_3 \qquad \text{(Equation 4.4)}$$

Now, if the initial supply of carbonic acid (H_2CO_3) is exhausted by Reaction 4.3 and other similar weathering reactions before the initial supply of oxygen is exhausted by Reaction 4.4, then the Fe^{2+} will be oxidized (Reaction 4.4) and precipitate out in the soil. Conversely, if the initial supply of oxygen is exhausted first, then all the Fe^{2+} will remain in reduced form and therefore soluble and leach out of the soil. This will result in a *net loss of iron in the weathered rock* – just how great that loss of iron is will depend on how great the excess of H_2CO_3 is relative to O_2. Thus, the balance between H_2CO_3 and oxygen in the soil water is of crucial importance in determining the pattern of iron distribution in soil profiles.

We can define the parameter, R, to be the ratio of the oxygen demand of the rock for oxidation (expressed as D_{ox}), which is largely dependent on the Fe^{2+} content, to the carbonic acid demand for silicate/carbonate weathering (expressed as D_{ac}) to cause a net loss of iron in any particular rock type. (Note that one of the major assumptions here is that weathering is only due to carbonic acid.)

$$R = \frac{D_{ox}}{D_{ac}} \qquad\qquad \text{(Equation 4.5)}$$

If the measured value of R for the soil water is less than the value of R for a rock, the soils derived from that rock will be depleted in iron. Values of R for any particular rock type can be estimated by analysis of its chemical composition.

Rocks differ enormously in their compositions. Of particular interest in the present context are the iron content of the rock and the oxidation level of that iron. Thus, for every different rock type there will be a different balance between the proportions of O_2 and H_2CO_3 in the soil water that will lead to a net loss of iron on weathering. Consider a rock containing 10% total iron. If this iron were mostly in reduced form (ferrous iron), on weathering it would relatively easily use up the oxygen available in solution, so that the remaining iron could be removed by acid in solution. Thus, a significant loss of iron would result from the consumption of only a relatively small proportion of carbonic acid. If the iron were mostly in the insoluble, oxidized (ferric) form, then significant iron loss could only take place if there were not much oxygen around (which would lead to production of yet more insoluble iron oxides), but a greater proportion of carbonic acid to leach out any reduced (ferrous) iron present.

- ▪ Two rocks A and B have R values of 1 and 10, respectively, calculated from their composition. Which rock would need more carbonic acid to bring about a net iron loss on weathering, assuming the atmospheric conditions are the same?

- ▪ Rock A has a much lower value of R than rock B; thus its carbonic acid demand relative to its oxygen demand is much higher – so rock A will need a larger amount of acid for net iron loss than rock B.

The Denison and Pronto paleosols

Within 30 km of the northern shore of Lake Huron in Ontario, Canada are two paleosols – the Denison and the Pronto paleosols. These provide valuable insights into the information about the chemistry of ancient atmospheres that can be gleaned from soils, and show some of the difficulties involved. Both paleosols are about 2.4 billion years old, and each forms a layer ranging in thickness from a few centimetres to about 20 m at the boundary between two major geological features, i.e. where Huronian sediments overlie older Archean rocks (Figure 4.11). The Pronto paleosol was formed by deep weathering of granitic rocks, while the Denison paleosol resulted from weathering of 'greenstones' – rocks that were originally volcanic in origin similar to lavas from modern volcanoes.

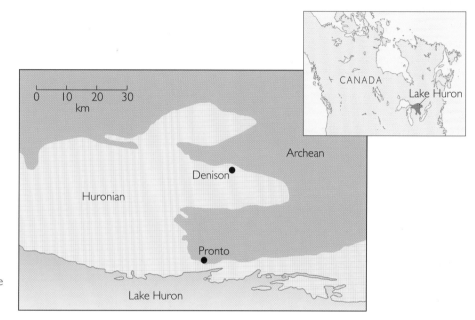

Figure 4.11
Sketch map showing the locations of the Pronto and Denison paleosols at the base of the Huronian sequence in Ontario, Canada.

Table 4.2 (overleaf) sets out the compositions of the Denison and Pronto paleosols and the rocks from which they were derived. According to geological convention, elements are quoted in Table 4.2 as their oxides. This can be confusing, since some oxides such as TiO_2 do actually occur in that form in rocks, while others such as Na_2O cannot. Recall that an element such as iron may be present in a number of different minerals in the same rock, and it may be present in either Fe^{2+} or Fe^{3+} form in each mineral. While there may not be any iron oxides present *as such* in the rock, the total of all the Fe^{2+} present in all minerals is expressed as FeO, while the total of all the Fe^{3+} present is expressed as Fe_2O_3.

- What is the difference in total iron (FeO + Fe_2O_3) between the Denison paleosol and its source rock? Which ion (Fe^{2+} or Fe^{3+}) is predominantly responsible for this difference?

- The total iron content is much lower in the Denison paleosol than in the source rock. The percentage of ferric iron (Fe_2O_3) is broadly similar in both the soil and rock, while the percentage of ferrous iron (FeO) is markedly less in the soil relative to the rock. So, the decrease in the percentage *total* iron in the paleosol must be due to removal of ferrous iron, FeO.

Table 4.2 Average composition (in mass %) of the Denison and Pronto paleosols, and their source rocks. Iron is calculated as both the ferrous Fe(II) form, FeO, and the ferric Fe(III) form, Fe_2O_3. (According to geological convention, elements are quoted as oxides, but do not be distracted by this. The soil samples were taken from near the surface.)

Elements present (in terms of oxide)	Denison paleosol	Denison greenstone source rock	Pronto paleosol	Pronto granitic source rock
SiO_2	63.9	51.4	66.9	73.7
Al_2O_3	21.0	10.2	15.1	11.5
TiO_2	0.9	2.0	0.5	0.1
FeO	1.9	12.5	0.6	0.6
Fe_2O_3	2.6	3.3	6.4	0.2
total iron (FeO + Fe_2O_3)	**4.5**	**15.8**	**7.0**	**0.8**
MgO	0.9	12.8	0.6	0.4
CaO	0.1	1.1	0.25	0.3
Na_2O	0.4	0.7	0.3	4.2
K_2O	5.9	0.7	5.0	5.4
P_2O_5	0.3	0.4	0.2	0.6
MnO	0.02	0.2	0.01	0.01
H_2O	2.4	4.8	4.4	3.2

This loss of ferrous iron without a corresponding increase in ferric iron, might lead one to conclude from this that the atmosphere was clearly reducing when the Denison paleosol formed. But this conclusion would be hasty.

▨   What is the difference in total iron (FeO + Fe_2O_3) between the Pronto paleosol and its source rock? Which ion (Fe^{2+} or Fe^{3+}) is predominantly responsible for this difference?

▨   The total iron content is very much higher in the Pronto paleosol than in the source rock. In this case, almost all of the difference is due to ferric iron, Fe_2O_3.

Clearly, then there were large differences in the behaviour of iron when the Denison greenstone and the Pronto granite were weathered. These differences are reflected in the soil profiles of the resulting paleosols in Figure 4.12. In the case of the Denison paleosol, the extensive leaching of ferrous iron (FeO) *superficially* suggests a reducing atmosphere (i.e. the ferrous iron has not been oxidized at the soil surface), while for the Pronto paleosol the enrichment in ferric iron (Fe_2O_3) at the soil surface suggests an oxidizing one. But this cannot be possible, as the two soils formed at the same time, under similar atmospheric conditions.

This apparent paradox can be resolved by looking more closely at the composition of the source rocks themselves and the weathering process. In the Denison greenstone, the ratio of Fe^{2+} to Fe^{3+} is almost 4 : 1, whereas in the Pronto granite it is about 3 : 1, but the Pronto granite has much less *total* iron.

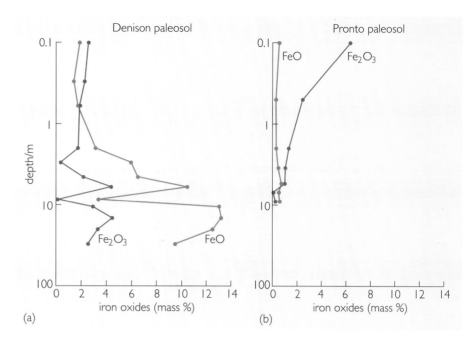

Figure 4.12
Variations in ferrous iron (expressed as FeO) and ferric iron (expressed as Fe_2O_3) with depth below the surface of the Denison and Pronto paleosols. Both soils are the same age, and formed within 30 km of each other (Figure 4.11).

■   Bearing in mind the earlier discussion of the roles of carbonic acid and oxygen in weathering, what can you conclude about the apparently reducing conditions suggested by the Denison paleosol?

■   When the iron-rich Denison greenstone was weathered, forming the paleosol, much more Fe^{2+} was liberated by carbonic acid than when the iron-poor Pronto granite was weathered; indeed, more Fe^{2+} was released in solution than could be oxidized by the available oxygen in the reducing conditions.

Thus, the soil profiles in Figure 4.12 tell us more about the ratio of oxygen to carbonic acid in soil water required to weather rocks than they do about atmospheric oxygen directly. Chemical studies show that the R value for the Denison greenstone is about 0.06, while that for the Pronto granite is about 0.006. Because R is the ratio of oxygen to carbonic acid required to cause a net iron loss in a given rock type, it follows that the ratio of dissolved oxygen to carbon dioxide in soil water when the soils were formed 2.4 billion years ago must have fallen within the range 0.06 to 0.006. Because iron loss occurred in the Denison paleosol, but not in the Pronto, the actual ratio of oxygen to carbon dioxide in the rainwater must have been less than the R value for the Denison greenstone but greater than that for the Pronto granite. As carbon dioxide is more soluble in water than is oxygen, it can be shown from this range of R values for the rainwater that the ratio of oxygen to carbon dioxide *in the atmosphere* must have been between 0.2 and 2 at the time the paleosols were formed. Today, the ratio of these gases in the atmosphere is close to 600 : 1.

We can conclude, then, that when the two paleosols formed more than 2 billion years ago, the atmosphere may have been oxidizing overall, but that there was far less oxygen relative to carbon dioxide than in the present atmosphere. You will have gleaned from the Pronto and Denison case study that the chemistry of paleosols is complex, and inferences about atmospheric composition from them are indirect. But when other paleosols from around the world are examined, a consistent picture emerges: all the well-studied paleosols less than 1.9 billion years old are highly oxidized. The difference between pre-2.2-billion-year-old paleosols (like the Denison and Pronto) and post-1.9-billion-year-old paleosols is striking, and suggests that there was a marked change in weathering processes, which is best explained by a sharp increase in atmospheric oxygen. One estimate is that atmospheric oxygen levels rose from about 0.2% to about 3% (0.01 PAL to about 0.14 PAL) between 2.2 and 1.9 billion years ago.

4.3 Evidence from uranium deposits

Further evidence that a significant change took place in the atmosphere about 2 billion years ago comes from sedimentary rocks found near Blind River and Elliott Lake in Ontario, Canada. These rocks contain deposits of **uraninite**, an important ore of uranium and other scarce elements such as radium. What, then, can these deposits tell us about the history of oxygen in the atmosphere?

To understand the evidence, you need to know a little about the chemical properties of uranium. We have seen that iron exists in red beds and BIFs in its oxidized ferric form, Fe(III), which is extremely insoluble in water. Only in its reduced ferrous form, Fe(II), can iron be dissolved and so transported in solution. Uranium shows an inverse relationship: its *reduced* form, U(IV), is extremely insoluble, whereas its *oxidized* form, U(VI), is soluble enough to be transported in solution.

Pitchblende, the ore from which metallic uranium is commonly extracted, contains uraninite, which is a complex oxide with a composition that can be roughly represented as U_3O_8, i.e. $UO_2.2UO_3$.

- ▨   Is U_3O_8 the fully oxidized form of uranium?

- ▪   No, not entirely – the fully oxidized form of uranium, U(VI), yields the oxide UO_3, while the reduced form, U(IV), gives UO_2. Both oxides are present in association in U_3O_8.

Uraninite, then, is a partially-reduced complex oxide of uranium, and so is not stable in contact with today's oxidizing atmosphere. Thus, a piece of uraninite ore left out in the open would gradually be oxidized and, as it became oxidized, it would become soluble – and eventually be entirely leached away. Now the interesting thing about the Ontario uraninite deposits is that they are clearly of *detrital* origin – i.e. the uraninite had been weathered out of older rocks, transported by streams and re-deposited *unchanged* in new sediments. Convincing evidence for this process comes from the grains of uraninite themselves – they are rounded like grains of sand, a characteristic feature of a detrital origin. Sedimentologists estimate that it would have taken about 100 years for the grains to be derived from their source regions, carried in rivers, and re-deposited. The uraninite grains could not have survived for that length of time in an atmosphere that was as oxidizing as today's. Calculations based on the sizes of the grains suggest that the atmosphere at that time must have contained less than about 0.1–1% oxygen.

If the Ontario deposits were unique, they might not be meaningful. But they are not – deposits of uraninite occur elsewhere in the world, *exclusively* in rocks older than 2 billion years. There are some important deposits in the Witwatersrand Basin of South Africa, associated with the world-famous gold deposits which are also of detrital origin. Uraninite deposits, then, indicate that prior to about 2 billion years ago, the Earth's atmosphere was not strongly oxidizing, probably containing less than 0.1–1% oxygen.

It follows that as the atmosphere became more oxidizing about 2 billion years ago (as we have seen from other evidence in the rock record), detrital uraninite deposits could no longer have been formed, as any uraninite in contact with the atmosphere would have been oxidized; it would then have dissolved and been transported in solution, blending with all the other material transported by rivers to the sea. However, we know from the 1.8-billion-year-old deposits such as those found at Oklo in Gabon, Africa, that some uranium did not share that fate. When uranium, in oxidized form, is transported in solution through porous young rocks, it may encounter organic material in the form of rotting vegetation; bacterial processes involved in the decay of the vegetation use up all the available oxygen and create a locally reducing environment. Under these conditions, the uranium would be reduced and would therefore be deposited. Through time, this could lead to large local concentrations of uranium, such as those found at Oklo in Gabon.

If a sufficient mass of the radioactive uranium isotope (^{235}U) accumulates, a spontaneous chain reaction can ensue. This is what is thought to have happened in the deposits at Oklo – these deposits could, in effect, be regarded as 'the world's first nuclear reactor'. It is possible that the chain reactions may have continued gently for many years, generating nothing more spectacular than gentle heating of the surrounding deposits. Clear evidence that the uranium in these deposits had 'gone critical' long before it was mined is provided by its isotopic composition – in many places the ore is severely depleted in ^{235}U, which had decayed long ago to different daughter products.

Because radioactive isotopes decay spontaneously through time, natural uranium today contains only a tiny proportion (about 0.7%) of ^{235}U. However, 1.8 billion years ago when the deposits at Oklo accumulated, ^{235}U would have formed a far higher proportion of the element. Thus, it would have been easier for sufficient ^{235}U to come together to initiate a chain reaction.

Question 4.3
Given that today's atmosphere is oxidizing, is there anything to prevent Oklo-type uranium concentrations from forming today and going critical?

4.4 Inferences from mantle oxidation

One curious feature of the Earth is that its mantle – which comprises a large fraction of the Earth's volume (see Figure 1.1) – is oxidized. The mantle consists of silicate minerals, and all of its iron is present as silicates or oxides – there is no metallic iron in the mantle at all. This is curious because the Earth's core *is* metallic iron; moreover, meteorites – which are samples of the materials from which the Earth was made – also contain metallic iron (for example, see Figure 4.13) and reduced sulfide minerals. It seems plausible, then, that the mantle of the early Earth was in a more reduced state than it is today. Indeed, BIFs provide evidence for a more reduced mantle on the early Earth, since their formation involved huge amounts of reduced iron being pumped into the oceans from hydrothermal vents at mid-ocean ridges.

If the mantle became progressively more oxidized through time, it could have *indirectly* affected atmospheric oxygen levels. Now, mantle oxidation would not have taken place through mantle–atmosphere interactions as the mantle is not in direct contact with the atmosphere. Rather interactions between the mantle and the hydrosphere would have been responsible. At subduction zones, some water might, by analogy with present-day processes, have been carried down into the mantle in

Figure 4.13
A polished surface of a pallasite meteorite. Pallasites consist of roughly equal proportions of metallic iron (grey) and olivine crystals (amber brown), some of them fragmented and invaded by iron.

the form of hydrated minerals in basalt. Deep within the mantle, these minerals might have become dehydrated, releasing water directly into the mantle. *If* there were reduced iron minerals present in the mantle, as evidence suggests, some of these minerals would have been oxidized and hydrogen gas would have been liberated.

If this reaction took place, volcanoes around the world would exhale a proportion of hydrogen gas. This hydrogen would then be rapidly oxidized back to water by any oxygen in the atmosphere – the hydrogen would simply burn in volcanic vents. In fact, tiny amounts of gas burning with a distinctive blue flame (indicating the presence of hydrogen) have often been observed at basaltic volcanoes such as Kilauea in Hawaii. One (very rough) estimate suggests that about 2.4×10^8 kg of hydrogen are exhaled by volcanoes each year at present.

As long as mantle oxidation continued, it could put a brake on the accumulation of atmospheric oxygen. Although there is no *direct* evidence, some scientists believe that atmospheric oxygen levels did not begin to rise until about 2 billion years ago, by which time the mantle was approaching its current oxidation state.

4.5 Looking back to the very beginning

As we peer back in time beyond 2 billion years ago, our view darkens. Very ancient rocks are scarce at the Earth's surface, and those we can find tell us little about the atmosphere that was present at that time – they record information about conditions at depths of many kilometres into the Earth's crust.

Unaltered sediments are also rare. Rocks of the Warrawoona Group in Australia contain some clues to the early conditions, in the form of gypsum rosettes (calcium sulfate), and other rocks contain evidence of halite (common salt, $NaCl$) crystals. Today, these minerals are commonly formed in saline basins such as the Dead Sea. Hence, their presence in ancient rocks suggests that when 3.5-billion-year-old seawater evaporated, it had a chemistry broadly similar to that of modern seawater. Unfortunately, evaporite minerals are better indicators of surface temperature than of atmospheric chemistry. We can speculate from these observations that a temperature greater than 25 °C is likely to have prevailed at Warrawoona, and that the atmosphere was probably weakly reducing or neutral.

There are no rocks older than about 3.8–4 billion years, so the physical record ceases then. There is therefore a 800–600-million-year-long 'dark age' between the time when the Earth formed, 4.6 billion years ago, and the age of the oldest rocks. We have no *direct* evidence of the composition of Earth's atmosphere during this time – the Hadean Era. In Greek mythology Hades was the Underworld; the abode of departed spirits, and in more modern usage is often identified with Hell. Conditions on Earth must indeed have been hellish, because at that time the Earth was still experiencing devastating bombardment by asteroids as the process of accretion from planetary debris waned. Some scientists have argued that life was not able to establish a successful foothold on Earth until that bombardment ceased. It may have evolved more than once previously, only to be literally blown out of the water by massive impacts.

4.6 A synthesis

Taken together, the various strands of evidence from the rock record that we have discussed in this chapter point to a significant increase in atmospheric oxygen levels about 2 billion years ago (see the summary of this evidence in Table 4.3), but what else can be said about the oxygen levels in the early atmosphere?

The American atmospheric scientist Jim Kasting has proposed a three-stage, 'three-box' summary model to describe the evolution of the atmosphere (Figure 4.14). His three 'boxes' are the atmosphere, the surface ocean and the deep ocean, each of which constitutes a distinct reservoir of oxygen. During Stage I, which persisted until about 2.4 to 2 billion years ago, all three reservoirs were essentially anoxic (reducing). This is indicated by the absence of red beds and the preservation of detrital uranium minerals.

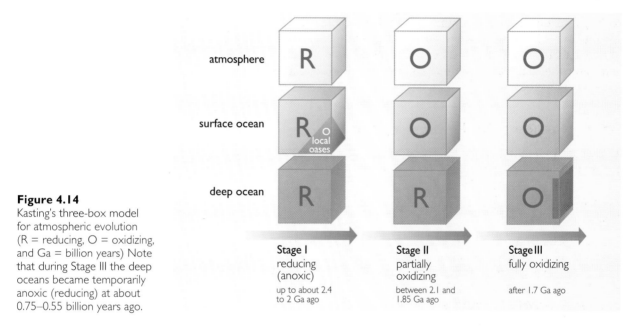

Figure 4.14
Kasting's three-box model for atmospheric evolution (R = reducing, O = oxidizing, and Ga = billion years) Note that during Stage III the deep oceans became temporarily anoxic (reducing) at about 0.75–0.55 billion years ago.

Table 4.3 Summary of evidence from the rock record.

Source of evidence	Evidence	Inference
red beds	most are less than 2 Ga old	atmosphere became more oxidizing after 2 Ga ago
BIFs	most are more than 2 Ga old	atmosphere was reducing or at most very weakly oxidizing before 2 Ga ago; shallow marine basins were oxidizing; while deep oceans were anoxic
paleosols	those less than 1.9 Ga old are highly oxidized	suggests a marked change in atmospheric conditions between 1.9 and 2.2 Ga ago
	those more than 2.2 Ga old are less oxidized	
deposits containing detrital uraninite	all are more than 2 Ga old	formed in a reducing/weakly oxidizing atmosphere; atmosphere became more oxidizing after about 2 Ga ago
the mantle	no *direct* evidence	mantle approached its present oxidation state about 2 Ga ago

On the Stage I Earth, where volcanism was more vigorous than it is now, hydrothermal vents ('black smokers') delivered vast amounts of reduced ferrous iron into the deep oceans. Any dissolved oxygen was consumed in oxidation reactions, so the entire ocean was anoxic, apart from local 'oases' of shallow surface ocean waters where photosynthesizing organisms flourished. Some of the oxygen these organisms produced was used in forming BIFs, and the rest was mopped up immediately in oxidizing the reduced gases such as hydrogen that were exhaled by volcanoes, and in other inorganic sinks.

In Stage II, between about 2.1 and 1.85 billion years ago, the atmosphere was oxidizing, but the oceans may have been stratified, with anoxic deep waters overlain by oxygenated surface waters. Both BIFs *and* red beds were widely deposited, indicating that the deep oceans were anoxic (BIFs), while the land surface and shallow continental basins were not (BIFs and red beds). There must also have been a prodigious source of reduced iron in the deep oceans to create the large quantites of BIFs formed at this time.

The end of Stage II was marked by the virtual disappearance of BIFs from the rock record about 1.7 billion years ago. Activity at hydrothermal vents had probably waned somewhat, limiting the supply of reduced iron into the deep oceans, while the gradually increasing atmospheric oxygen levels probably resulted in 'clearing out of the backlog' of reduced iron from the oceans via precipitation. Note that towards the end of the neo-Proterozoic (0.75–0.55 billion years ago), there was a brief but important worldwide episode of BIF deposition, indicating that the deep oceans may have become temporarily anoxic again.

During Stage III, all three reservoirs (i.e. atmosphere, surface ocean and deep ocean) were fully oxidizing, as on the modern Earth.

This model provides a useful description of the evolution of the atmosphere, and summarizes the diverse evidence from the rock record and other sources that we have discussed in this chapter. We shall make use of other models in later chapters.

4.7 Summary of Chapter 4

1   Several strands of evidence in the rock record indicate that a major increase in atmospheric oxygen occurred about 2 billion years ago.

2   Red beds, which are less than 2 billion years old, are conspicuous components of the rock record. Although the origin of the red colour is complex, it is indicative of an oxidizing environment. They originated in lakes or on river beds, i.e. they are non-marine.

3   The origin of banded iron formations (BIFs) is somewhat puzzling, but the huge scale of BIFs requires global-scale processes. BIFs were deposited in shallow marine basins. Hydrothermal vents in the deep ocean probably were the source of reduced iron, which was deposited subsequently in the oxidized form in the iron-rich layers in BIFs. BIFs are predominantly more than 2 billion years old.

4   The extent of iron leaching in paleosols provides important indirect clues to atmospheric composition. Whether or not iron leaching takes place depends on the oxidation state of the iron in the source rock, and the relative proportions of iron, oxygen and carbon dioxide in the associated soil water. Globally, paleosols suggest a striking change to a more oxygen-rich atmosphere about 2 billion years ago.

5 Whereas ferric oxides (i.e. the more oxidized form) are usually highly insoluble, uranium oxides are only soluble in their most oxidized form. A sample of uraninite, the ore of uranium, exposed to an oxidizing atmosphere such as today's, would be oxidized and removed in solution. Thus, ore deposits containing grains of detrital uraninite must have been formed in reducing conditions. These deposits are all more than about 2 billion years old.

6 It is thought that the Earth's mantle was approaching its current oxidation state by 2 billion years ago, and that this allowed the atmospheric oxygen levels to begin to rise, although there is no direct evidence.

7 Kasting's three-box model provides a useful description of atmospheric evolution. The three boxes are the atmosphere, the surface ocean and the deep ocean. In Stage I, all three boxes are reducing, in Stage II only the deep ocean remains reducing, and in Stage III all three boxes are oxidizing.

Now try the following questions to consolidate your understanding of this chapter.

Question 4.4
The absence of red beds more than 2 billion years old from the rock record is significant. But why should one treat this – and other 'negative' lines of evidence – with caution?

Question 4.5
Two source rocks have the same total iron content, but have developed different soil profiles in a slightly oxidizing atmosphere. In three or four sentences, explain how this might be possible.

Chapter 5
Evolution of the Earth's atmosphere during the Cryptozoic

5.1 Introduction

We have now completed our review of the physical record of atmospheric oxygen levels preserved in rocks and fossils as far back as 3.8–4 billion years ago. Although patchy, the overall picture that has emerged is of an early, oxygen-poor atmosphere, with a significant increase in the atmospheric oxygen level occurring about 2 billion years ago, and a much larger increase during the early Phanerozoic. But that leaves unanswered the question of what happened in the period before the rock record commenced about 4 billion years ago. This is difficult to investigate, because rather than considering tangible evidence, we have to evaluate complex – and sometimes speculative – interactions between organic and inorganic processes. However, some intriguing conclusions and profound questions emerge.

In this chapter we shall investigate the underlying processes acting during the Cryptozoic (from the formation of the Earth to 540 million years ago) that brought about the oxygen levels indicated by the rock and fossil records. We start, in Section 5.2, with the earliest atmosphere of all – that which occurred soon after the Earth was formed. We then look at the source of the earliest (non-photosynthetic) oxygen in the atmosphere (Section 5.3), and the likely fate of oxygen in the early atmospheric cycles (Section 5.4). In Section 5.5 we use the carbon isotope data that was introduced in Section 3.3 to chart the subsequent rise of oxygen levels through the Proterozoic. This leads to some fundamental links between oxygen levels and geological processes.

5.2 Early atmospheres

5.2.1 Primary atmospheres

Planetary scientists make a distinction between the primary and secondary atmosphere of a planet. The **primary atmosphere** existed immediately after the formation of the planet; the **secondary atmosphere** was then acquired as the result of subsequent changes. As we saw in *Origins of Earth and Life*, the Earth's primary atmosphere was formed, along with the Earth itself, by accretion from the primitive solar nebula. The nebula was dominated by hydrogen and helium; therefore, hydrogen and helium (and traces of many other gases) were probably present in roughly cosmic proportions in the Earth's earliest atmosphere.

All the early gases that constituted the primary atmospheres were stripped away during the final stages of the birth of the Sun, when a great blast known as the T Tauri wind swept outwards through the Solar System. Many stars like the Sun pass through a stage like this when they are about a million years old: they eject matter at a prodigious rate, losing as much as half a solar mass per million years in solar winds blowing at $100–200\,km\,s^{-1}$. The fierce T Tauri wind would have blown any solid objects less than about 10 m in diameter clear out of the Solar System, and stripped the infant inner planets of their primary atmospheres. The final stages in the formation of the planets would only have occurred once the T Tauri wind had blown itself out. It is in these closing moments in the formation of the Solar System that we can trace the birth of our present atmosphere: it is very much a secondary atmosphere.

5.2.2 Secondary atmospheres

Mercury, Earth, Venus and Mars (the terrestrial planets) are similar planets located in the inner part of the Solar System, so it is reasonable to suppose that they all started off with broadly similar atmospheres. The volatile components (often simply called 'volatiles') in the atmospheres of these planets – such as water, carbon dioxide and nitrogen – may well have originated in three ways:

◆　The volatiles may have been present as components of the essentially 'rocky' planetesimals from which the terrestrial planets originated. These planetesimals would have formed in the *inner* regions of the Solar System and may have been richer in volatiles in the relatively cooler regions further from the Sun and less rich in volatiles in regions nearer to the Sun. Water would have been chemically bound into the crystal structure of the hydrated minerals of the planetesimals, and carbon and nitrogen would have been present in complex organic compounds.

◆　The volatiles may have come from planetesimals that originated in the *outer* (and, therefore, cooler) parts of the Solar System (the asteroid belt or beyond). In this case, any carbon and nitrogen would have been present in complex organic molecules or as methane and ammonia ices, and the water may have been present largely as ice. Accretion of the volatile-rich planetesimals continued very late in the growth of the planets: in one sense, it still continues to the present-day as carbonaceous meteorites still arrive bearing volatile components.

◆　Formation of the terrestrial planets' secondary atmospheres was intimately linked to their own internal differentiation. It is likely that all the terrestrial planets underwent some form of internal differentiation similar to the process that is known to have occurred on the Earth. Isotopic studies suggest that accretion of the Earth lasted about 150 million years, and that the core was established by about 4.41 billion years ago. Formation of the core involved a massive redistribution of material within the Earth, and as a result, immense heating occurred. During this massive upheaval, coupled with the collision event that formed the Moon, volatile materials that had been trapped within the Earth when accretion took place were released. This large-scale **outgassing** of volatiles is thought to have formed our atmosphere and oceans.

Thus, there were several possible origins for the gases in the secondary atmospheres of the terrestrial planets. But once these gases had reached the surface of a planet, what was to stop them from leaking away into space?

Ultimately, it is the strength of a planet's gravitational field and its temperature that dictate whether a particular gas can be retained on that planet. In order for any object – gas molecule or spacecraft – to escape the gravitational clutches of a planet, its velocity much reach a certain minimum, the **escape velocity**, v_{esc}, which is determined by properties of the planet itself. For a planet of mass M and radius R, v_{esc} is given by:

$$v_{esc} = \sqrt{\frac{2GM}{R}}$$

(Equation 5.1)

where G is the Universal Gravitational Constant. Therefore, planets that differ in size will have different escape velocities. The velocity of gas molecules depends on their mass and the temperature of the gas. So, it is theoretically possible to calculate which gases in a planet's atmosphere could be retained for geologically significant lengths of time.

Although it is likely that the terrestrial planets started off with similar secondary atmospheres, their atmospheres evolved differently because of variations in escape velocity and in their geological histories (Table 5.1). These differences may have resulted from a number of processes. Net loss of gases into space is important on small planets such as Mars, as they are not massive enough to retain gases gravitationally. Other atmospheric gases that do not escape may react chemically with surface rocks, or with each other, especially when these reactions are promoted by powerful solar radiation. While some gases are lost from the atmosphere of the terrestrial planets, others are added as they are outgassed from the interior of the planets. As Table 5.1 shows, there are large variations between the *present* atmospheres of the four terrestrial planets – so large that it is not immediately obvious what connections there are between them.

Table 5.1 Estimated compositions of the atmospheres of the terrestrial planets immediately after their formation, after the first billion years, and at present. The compositions are given in bars, where 1 bar is the Earth's *present* atmospheric pressure, or as a ratio.

Planet	Atmospheric composition/bar			
	4.6×10^9 years ago	3.6×10^9 years ago	Processes that have taken place over the last 3.6×10^9 years	Present day
Mercury	CO_2 5 H_2O 25 N_2 0.15	CO_2 5 H_2O 25 N_2 0.15	runaway greenhouse, so all volatiles lost to space	minute amounts of He, Na, O from the solar wind, etc.
Venus	CO_2 90 H_2O 450 N_2 3	CO_2 1 $H_2O : CO_2 > 1$ N_2 1	moist runaway greenhouse, so almost all water lost to space	CO_2 90 $H_2O : CO_2 \ll 1$ N_2 3
Earth*	CO_2 60 H_2O 300 N_2 2	CO_2 1 $H_2O : CO_2 \ll 1$ N_2 1	CO_2 falls, O_2 rises	CO_2 0.00036 H_2O 0.01–0.04 N_2 0.78 O_2 0.21
Mars	CO_2 10 H_2O 50 N_2 0.3	CO_2 2 $H_2O : CO_2 \ll 1$ N_2 0.2	loss of CO_2 and N_2 to the surface of the planet and to space	CO_2 0.007 O_2 trace N_2 0.002

*Some authors suggest that there could have been a component of SO_2 and less water present 4.6 billion years ago.

5.2.3 Formation of the Earth's secondary atmosphere

Two of the radioactive decay processes that take place in the Earth's mantle involve, respectively, radioactive potassium, ^{40}K, and radioactive iodine, ^{129}I. Now, ^{40}K (with a half-life of 1.28 billion years) decays rather slowly to form the noble gas argon, ^{40}Ar, whereas ^{129}I (with a half-life of 17.2 million years) decays relatively rapidly to the noble gas xenon, ^{129}Xe. The short half-life of ^{129}I means that ^{129}I has long been extinct in the Solar System.

We can, in fact, use the ^{40}K/^{40}Ar and ^{129}I/^{129}Xe isotope pairs to pin down the timing of the Earth's outgassing. We know that no ^{40}K and ^{129}I have been added since the Earth formed, so all the ^{40}Ar and ^{129}Xe present in the Earth's mantle must have come from the decay of the original radioactive ^{40}K and ^{129}I that were trapped in the mantle during the accretion of the Earth. However, this is complicated slightly by the fact that not all the ^{129}Xe present in the Solar System was derived from ^{129}I; ^{129}Xe was also formed in nucleosynthetic processes (a form of fusion reaction) shortly before the Solar System formed.

If the Earth outgassed in a *single* event (expelling all the trapped gases in one go) during or soon after its accretion, the atmosphere formed at that time would contain no ^{40}Ar, but would contain some ^{129}Xe.

▨ How can you account for this difference?

▨ There would have been no time for any ^{40}K to decay to ^{40}Ar, but some ^{129}Xe would already have been present due to nucleosynthetic processes.

Figure 5.1
Schematic representation of *hypothetical* variations in ^{129}Xe and ^{40}Ar in the Earth's mantle over the course of geological time, assuming that no outgassing had taken place since the Earth's formation 4.6 billion years (4.6 Ga) ago and that no ^{129}Xe due to nucleosynthetic processes had been present when the Earth formed.

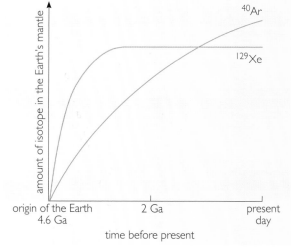

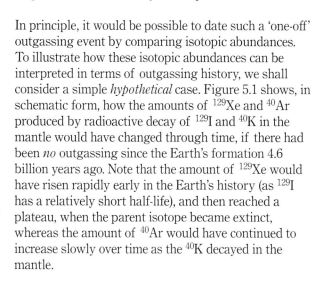

In principle, it would be possible to date such a 'one-off' outgassing event by comparing isotopic abundances. To illustrate how these isotopic abundances can be interpreted in terms of outgassing history, we shall consider a simple *hypothetical* case. Figure 5.1 shows, in schematic form, how the amounts of ^{129}Xe and ^{40}Ar produced by radioactive decay of ^{129}I and ^{40}K in the mantle would have changed through time, if there had been *no* outgassing since the Earth's formation 4.6 billion years ago. Note that the amount of ^{129}Xe would have risen rapidly early in the Earth's history (as ^{129}I has a relatively short half-life), and then reached a plateau, when the parent isotope became extinct, whereas the amount of ^{40}Ar would have continued to increase slowly over time as the ^{40}K decayed in the mantle.

Question 5.1

Assume for the sake of argument, that total outgassing of the Earth took place in a single event about 2 billion years (2 Ga) ago. Sketch a graph similar to that in Figure 5.1 to show what the development of ^{129}Xe and ^{40}Ar isotopes in the mantle would look like. (This is only a hypothetical question – there was no major outgassing event 2 billion years ago.)

However, life is not as simple as this – some outgassing has continued to the present day: indeed a proportion of the gases exhaled by volcanoes comes directly from the mantle. By analysing these volcanic gases and so comparing the ratios of ^{40}Ar and ^{129}Xe in mantle-derived rocks, it has been estimated that about 80–85% of our atmosphere was outgassed extremely early in Earth history; the remainder has been released slowly and steadily over the last 4.4 billion years, through volcanic activity.

Table 5.2 shows, among other things, the typical composition of present-day terrestrial volcanic gases.

▨   Examine Table 5.2. Which planetary atmosphere does the gas exhaled from terrestrial volcanoes most resemble? If it does not match any of them, why not?

▨   It is not a particularly good match to any of them, largely, but not exclusively, because it contains so much water.

Table 5.2 Average compositions (in percentage by volume) of the present-day secondary atmospheres of Earth, Mars and Venus, and of the gases exhaled by present-day terrestrial volcanoes.

Gas	Earth (vol %)	Mars (vol %)	Venus (vol %)	Terrestrial volcanic gases* (vol %)
O_2	20.9	0.13	–	trace
CO_2	0.036	95	96	3.4
N_2	78.1	2.7	3.5	trace
H_2O	1.0	0.03	0.01	94.0
Ar	0.93	1.6	0.007	trace
SO_2	2×10^{-9}	–	0.015	1.3
HCl	–	–	trace	0.34
CO	1.2×10^{-5}	0.07	4×10^{-3}	0.15
Ne	1.9×10^{-3}	2.5×10^{-4}	5×10^{-4}	trace
O_3	$1 \times 10^{-5} - 1 \times 10^{-6}$	1×10^{-5}	–	trace

*Volcanic gases vary widely; this is a representative example from Momotombo, Nicaragua. (Some have more reduced gases present, e.g. H_2S.)

If the composition of the volcanic gases is recalculated *without* water, it takes on a much more 'planetary' aspect, and resembles the present atmospheres of Mars and Venus particularly in terms of the amount of CO_2 present. This re-adjustment is, in fact, valid because when a terrestrial volcano erupts, much of the water that condenses as visible steam clouds may be derived from shallow levels, near the vent, rather than deep within the Earth. It is water that once fell as rain, soaked into the ground and found its way into the vicinity of the volcano to be *recycled*. It does not represent a net *addition* to the atmosphere.

In the Earth's early history, its interior was hot, and volcanic activity was intense. Thus, whatever the nature of the atmosphere that resulted initially from planetary-scale outgassing linked to core formation, it continued to be modified by prodigious volcanic exhalations of carbon dioxide and water. On Earth, although its effects on the atmosphere are modest, outgassing via volcanoes is still a highly visible process – every photograph of an active volcano shows towering clouds of vapour belching into the atmosphere (Figure 5.2), and remote sensing satellites reveal the huge plumes of sulfur dioxide injected by large explosive eruptions.

5.3 Non-photosynthetic oxygen

Although there was an abundance of combined oxygen in the atmosphere of the early Earth in the form of CO_2 and H_2O, molecular oxygen, O_2, was scarce (Table 5.1), but it is likely that it was not *entirely* absent. We can never be sure of the pre-biotic oxygen level on Earth, but one estimate places it at around 2×10^{10} molecules m^{-3}, i.e. about 10^{-12}–10^{-14} PAL at ground level. To make molecular oxygen in the atmosphere, the bonds between carbon and oxygen, or between hydrogen and oxygen, have to be broken. This takes energy. We have concentrated so far on photosynthesis as though this were the *only* process that can generate molecular oxygen. There is, however, an inorganic (abiogenic) process that generates *traces* of molecular oxygen, through the interaction of sunlight with water.

Figure 5.2
Condensing steam and acid fumes rise from Mount Etna (Sicily), Europe's largest active volcano. Some gas is escaping from the summit vent, but the most prominent source is a 'parasitic vent' in the middle distance, from which lava flows are streaming. Mount Etna may erupt as much as 3.5×10^7 kg of carbon dioxide and 4×10^6 kg of sulfur dioxide *per day*. These figures represent nearly 0.1 and 1% of the global anthropogenic fluxes of these gases.

When high-energy, short-wavelength (ultraviolet) rays of sunlight are absorbed by water molecules high up in the Earth's atmosphere, some of the water molecules are split by means of a process known as **photolytic dissociation** into hydrogen and oxygen. Of course, photolytic dissociation does not happen instantaneously to every water molecule in the atmosphere, but rather it is a slow and steady process. Some of the hydrogen molecules formed as a result of photolytic dissociation are re-oxidized back to water, but other hydrogen molecules are readily lost to space from the upper atmosphere, as hydrogen gas is extremely light. This is a *permanent* loss. Oxygen molecules, which are heavier, remain in the atmosphere. Oxygen can also be produced by a similar photolytic process in which carbon dioxide breaks down, yielding carbon monoxide and oxygen.

Photolytic dissociation may seem less relevant to life than photosynthesis, but it is nonetheless an extremely important process. Venus at one time probably had as much water as Earth, but has lost almost *all* of it through photolytic dissociation, leaving a hot, desiccated planet. According to one estimate, the Earth may have lost as much as one-third of its original inventory of water in this way. At the present day, Mars' atmosphere contains a significant trace of oxygen – about 0.13% – which probably resulted from photolytic breakdown of carbon dioxide.

■   What would have been the fate of any oxygen atoms or molecules formed photolytically in the early atmosphere of the Earth?

■   Most free oxygen atoms would have been rapidly consumed in oxidizing reduced compounds in the atmosphere or on the surface.

It is likely that considerable quantities of reduced materials were around then, some of them produced by volcanoes. Modern volcanoes erupt small amounts of reduced gases such as hydrogen sulfide, H_2S, notorious for its 'rotten eggs' smell, and these are rapidly oxidized in the atmosphere:

$$\underbrace{2H_2S}_{\substack{\text{from} \\ \text{volcanoes}}} + \underbrace{3O_2}_{\substack{\text{in the} \\ \text{atmosphere}}} \longrightarrow 2H_2O + 2SO_2 \qquad \text{(Equation 5.2)}$$

Most scientists agree that on the early Earth, before conditions had become generally oxidizing, volcanoes exhaled far more reduced gases such as H_2S and erupted lavas containing much more reduced iron and sulfides than do modern ones, as the mantle was less oxidized at that time. These reduced gases and iron minerals provided crucially important 'sinks' for oxygen on the early, pre-biotic, Earth.

Question 5.2
Sunlight is potent stuff – it triggers innumerable chemical and physical processes in the atmosphere. Outline, in a couple of sentences, two interactions between sunlight and oxygen that are of profound current concern.

5.4 The early atmospheric cycles

With the evolution of life on Earth at the start of the Archean (about 3.8 billion years ago), photosynthesis became the main mechanism of oxygen generation, though photolytic dissociation still contributed a small amount of oxygen. In this section, we look quantitatively at the processes controlling the levels of oxygen (whether produced photolytically – abiogenically – or biologically) on the early Earth during the Archean (from 3.8 billion years ago to 2.5 billion years ago).

It is intuitively tempting to think of atmospheric oxygen levels as being dictated by biological processes alone. But, other things being equal, we already know that oxygen can only accumulate in the atmosphere when organic carbon is buried, and cannot use up oxygen. Carbon burial is essentially a *geological* process, whose tempo is driven by non-biological agencies.

Organic carbon burial does not take place uniformly. Despite the huge areas covered by deep-ocean basins, relatively little sediment accumulates in deep water. Instead, today, when continents cover about 30% of the Earth's surface, carbon burial takes place most efficiently in sediments deposited on continental shelves.

- ■ Can you suggest one such place where sediments are being deposited at the present day?

- ■ Deltas of major rivers such as the Amazon and Mississippi are huge sites of sediment deposition and, hence, of carbon burial.

Now, the continents on the early Earth (during the Archean) were much smaller than those of today. So, there were fewer great rivers, less extensive areas of continental shelf, and therefore less opportunity for sediment burial. There was also far less organic carbon being produced on the continents than later in the Earth's history. As the continents grew, the potential for carbon burial on continental shelf areas also grew. It is uncertain how fast the continents grew to their present size, but it is likely that they grew rapidly initially, and later slowed.

We saw in Section 3.4 that even the oldest sedimentary rocks (3.8–4 billion years old, deposited during the Archean) contain about 0.5–0.6% buried organic carbon (C_{org}). We shall not follow all the steps here, but it has been conservatively estimated that about 5–6×10^{10} kg of organic carbon (i.e. 4–5×10^{12} mole; where 1 mole of carbon $= 0.012$ kg) were buried each year during the Archean. This carbon probably represented about 20% of the total organic carbon produced. It therefore follows that the global primary productivity during the Archean was about 25–30×10^{10} kg carbon per year, or 2.0–2.5×10^{13} moles of carbon per year.

This primary productivity was the result of photosynthesis (Chapter 2):

$$\underbrace{n\mathrm{CO_2}}_{\substack{\text{in the}\\\text{atmosphere}}} + n\mathrm{H_2O} + \text{energy} \longrightarrow \underbrace{(\mathrm{CH_2O})_n}_{\text{biomass}} + \underbrace{n\mathrm{O_2}}_{\substack{\text{in the}\\\text{atmosphere}}} \qquad \text{(Equation 2.4)*}$$

▨ If $2.0\text{--}2.5 \times 10^{13}$ moles of organic carbon (biomass) were produced annually during this period, how much oxygen would enter the Earth's early atmosphere each year?

▨ One mole of oxygen is liberated when one mole of biomass is formed, so the same number of moles of oxygen would enter the atmosphere each year, i.e. $2.0\text{--}2.5 \times 10^{13}$ moles, assuming that all photosynthesis was oxygenic.

There is no a priori reason why early photosynthesizers should not have generated atmospheric oxygen at levels similar to those of today. Our problem, therefore, is given that despite the burial of organic carbon, the oxygen did not accumulate in the atmosphere, so *what happened to all the oxygen produced*? At the present day, oxygen production is balanced by aerobic respiration – the oxidation of biomass back into carbon dioxide and energy. Oxygen can only accumulate by burial of organic carbon. In the early Archean (about 3.5 billion years ago), however, the world was a different place: it was younger and more geologically active, and many of the metabolic pathways that are now important had not yet evolved – land plants, for example, had not evolved. If oxygen had accumulated to significant levels in the atmosphere, it would have been toxic to most simple organisms living then, which had evolved and thrived in an oxygen-free environment.

▨ Given the evidence for large-scale photosynthesis, and carbon burial through deposition of sediments during the Archean, why did oxygen not accumulate in the atmosphere?

▨ The oxygen must have been consumed by other processes, such as the oxidation of reduced volcanic gases and iron minerals. This would have been an entirely inorganic 'sink' for oxygen, which as we saw in Chapter 4, can be summarized as follows:

$$4\,\mathrm{Fe^{2+}} + \mathrm{O_2} + 8\,\mathrm{HCO_3^-} + 4\,\mathrm{H_2O} \longrightarrow 2\,\mathrm{Fe_2O_3} + 8\,\mathrm{H_2CO_3} \qquad \text{(Equation 4.4)*}$$

Equation 4.4 shows that for every mole of oxygen removed from the atmosphere, four moles of ferrous (reduced) iron would be oxidized. Therefore, if, as we have just calculated, $2.0\text{--}2.5 \times 10^{13}$ moles of oxygen were generated annually on the Archean Earth, and if, for the moment, we assume ferrous iron compounds were the *only* sink, this would mean that $8.0\text{--}10 \times 10^{13}$ moles of iron would have been oxidized annually. Therefore, a staggering 5×10^{12} kg of iron would probably have been deposited in oxidized form in sediments annually.

▨ It has been estimated that 1×10^{13} kg of sediments were deposited annually during the Archean. If iron were the only inorganic sink for oxygen on the early Earth, what fraction of these sediments would have been iron?

▨ The 'guesstimate' rate of iron oxidation (and deposition) calculated above was 5×10^{12} kg yr^{-1}. This is equivalent to $(5 \times 10^{12}$ kg yr$^{-1})/(1 \times 10^{13}$ kg yr$^{-1})$, i.e. 50% of the annual sedimentation rate during the Archean.

Now, even iron-rich BIFs contain, on average, only about 30% total iron, and most Archean sediments contain far less iron than this – only about 5%. So our crude back-of-envelope calculation suggests that iron oxidation could not have been the *only* sink for the Earth's oxygen.

An alternative sink might involve a different sort of biological activity to any we have yet discussed. So far we have focused on organisms that involve oxygen in their metabolism – photosynthesis and aerobic respiration – but there is another type of bacteria, capable of existence only in the *absence* of oxygen. One group of these anaerobic bacteria are **methanogenic** bacteria. They live by decomposing biomass to form carbon dioxide and methane (CH_4), both of which enter the atmosphere. The net reaction can be expressed as:

$$2(CH_2O)_n \longrightarrow nCH_4 + nCO_2$$ (Equation 5.3)

Methane produced in this way would be oxidized by any oxygen in the atmosphere:

$$CH_4 + 2O_2 \longrightarrow CO_2 + 2H_2O$$ (Equation 5.4)

Similar processes are known to take place at the Earth's surface today. For instance, stir up the organic sediment at the bottom of a stagnant pond, and you will see bubbles of methane ('marsh gas') coming to the surface. Spontaneous ignition of this methane to form transient flames is thought to give rise to ghostly lights known as the 'will-o'-the-wisp' that occasionally flicker over marshy areas.

Such anaerobic methanogenic bacteria may have returned almost as much carbon to the atmosphere (in the form of carbon dioxide and methane) as was 'fixed' by photosynthesis in the first place: they occupied an equivalent place in the early carbon cycle to that which the organisms involved in aerobic respiration do today. Methane is present in the modern atmosphere in only trace amounts (Table 1.1) – any that is manufactured today in swamps, marshes or rice paddies is rapidly oxidized to carbon dioxide and water (the residence time for methane in today's atmosphere is about 10 years). If, as seems likely, there were significant amounts of methane in the Earth's early, anoxic atmosphere, it may have had three effects:

- Oxidation of methane would have consumed oxygen produced by early oxygenic photosynthetic organisms, thus keeping atmospheric oxygen levels low.

- As a result, the absence of oxygen in Earth's primitive atmosphere would in turn have ensured the absence of ozone with its ability to screen out ultraviolet radiation.

- Methane, like carbon dioxide, is an efficient greenhouse gas. Thus, its presence, even at low levels, would have helped the Earth to remain warm during the Sun's faint, juvenile stages.

Some scientists argue that life could only have got started in water deep enough to provide protection from the Sun's short-wavelength glare. Methane itself does not provide an ideal screen against ultraviolet light, but it has been suggested that when irradiated in the atmosphere, it could have formed a 'smog' of organic compounds that provided an efficient screen. But this is speculative, as experimental studies have indicated that no such smog is formed in a weakly reducing atmosphere.

To sum up, at the time when reduced volcanic gases and iron consumed large amounts of oxygen in the Archean, methanogenic bacteria may also have played an important role by producing methane – another sink for oxygen. Therefore, atmospheric oxygen levels could not begin to rise on the Archean Earth until the rate of oxygen generation (and carbon burial) exceeded the rate at which reduced materials entered the surface environment and consumed oxygen.

▥   Can you suggest two circumstances that might have led to this changing balance?

▥   First, volcanic activity has declined through time (the Earth's internal processes are slowing down as it loses its radiogenic heat), so reduced materials would have been supplied less abundantly. Second, the supply of reduced gases from the mantle would have decreased in response to a change in the mantle's oxidation state as a result of subduction of hydrated minerals (Section 4.4).

5.5 Oxygen levels in the Proterozoic

Towards the end of the Archean, as the rock and fossil records indicate, oxygen levels did indeed begin to rise and then continued to do so during the next phase of the Earth's history – the Proterozoic (2500 million years ago to 540 million years ago). We shall now consider the build up of oxygen during the Proterozoic.

We have repeatedly stressed that oxygen can only accumulate in the atmosphere through burial of organic carbon; in fact, one could say that:

Each molecule of (buried) organic carbon represents a molecule of oxygen that either still exists, or has reacted with some oxidizable substance.

We shall focus on the geological processes of carbon burial and the growth of the crustal carbon reservoir. In Section 3.3 we encountered the Schidlowski diagram as evidence for the likely existence of early (oxygenic) photosynthetic organisms. We noted that the difference in isotopic composition (i.e. the difference in the $\delta^{13}C$ values) between the carbonate carbon (C_{carb}) and the organic carbon (C_{org}) reservoirs has been surprisingly constant throughout the Earth's history. We must now examine this remarkable situation more fully.

The absolute sizes of the C_{carb} and C_{org} reservoirs depend on global rates of erosion and sedimentation, and on recycling processes such as those taking place at the sea floor. We can summarize the entire carbon cycle at any particular time in the Earth's history as an isotopic mass balance:

$$\delta^{13}C_{in} = f_{carb}\delta^{13}C_{carb} + f_{org}\delta^{13}C_{org} \qquad \text{(Equation 5.5)}$$

where $\delta^{13}C_{in}$ is the average value of the isotopic composition of the carbon which has entered the Earth's surface environment, primarily from the mantle in the form of volcanic carbon dioxide; and f_{carb} and f_{org} are the fractions of the total quantity of carbon in the carbonate and organic reservoirs, respectively. This rather cryptic equation is more straightforward than it may appear. It merely states that the amount of carbon that has entered the Earth's environment ends up split between the carbonate and organic reservoirs. The fractions in the two reservoirs, f_{carb} and f_{org}, are interrelated, as there is no other source of carbon. When one of them increases, the other must decrease. Thus, $f_{carb} = 1 - f_{org}$.

Now, it is possible to measure directly the isotopic compositions of carbon, $\delta^{13}C_{in}$, entering the surface environment from the mantle in volcanic gases and it is found to be about –5‰. Average values of $\delta^{13}C_{carb}$ for the carbonate and $\delta^{13}C_{org}$ for the organic carbon reservoirs, respectively, can be measured directly from crustal sediments (or sedimentary rocks) of any given geological age. So, if we rearrange Equation 5.5, it is possible to calculate the fraction of the total carbon which is present in the organic reservoir (f_{org}) at any given point in geological history (as long as sedimentary rock samples are available for that time):

$$f_{org} = \frac{\delta^{13}C_{in} - \delta^{13}C_{carb}}{\delta^{13}C_{org} - \delta^{13}C_{carb}}$$ (Equation 5.6)

As we know the value of $\delta^{13}C_{in}$, Equation 5.6 reduces to:

$$f_{org} = \frac{-5\text{‰} - \delta^{13}C_{carb}}{\delta^{13}C_{org} - \delta^{13}C_{carb}}$$ (Equation 5.7)

Figure 5.3 shows the fraction of total carbon buried as organic carbon in sediments during the Proterozoic. As you can see, the value of f_{org} remains mostly between 0.1 and 0.2.

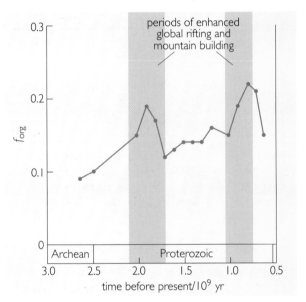

Figure 5.3
The fraction (f_{org}) of the total amount of carbon which is buried as organic carbon (biomass) during the Proterozoic (calculated from various sedimentary rocks of appropriate ages).

So far so good. However, f_{org}, the fraction of the total amount of carbon which is buried as organic carbon, is only part of the story.

■   In our pursuit of atmospheric oxygen levels, what do we need to know about the buried organic carbon reservoir apart from its *proportion* of the total carbon reservoir?

■   We need to know its *absolute* (total) mass.

Finding the size of the organic carbon reservoir at any particular time in the Earth's history requires some intricate calculations which are beyond the scope of this book. All we need to know, for present purposes, is that the size of the organic carbon reservoir, M, at any one time can be calculated using an equation that involves $\delta^{13}C_{carb}$, $\delta^{13}C_{org}$ and f_{org}. We can measure the first two of these quantities directly from sedimentary rocks of the appropriate age, and can derive f_{org} from Equation 5.6, so it is possible to find M. (If you are interested, the equation for calculating M is given in Box 5.1, but you will not be expected to memorize or recall it.) Although the scatter is very large as the original data from individual rocks vary considerably, some intriguing results emerge from such calculations (Figure 5.4).

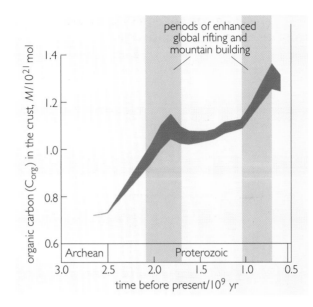

periods of enhanced
global rifting and
mountain building

Figure 5.4
The amount of buried
organic carbon (C_{org}) in the
crustal sediments during the
Proterozoic.

Box 5.1 Calculating the size of the organic carbon reservoir

The size of the organic carbon reservoir at any time in Earth's history can be calculated from:

$$M_{t-\tau} = M_t\,e^{-k\tau} + (\delta^{13}C_{carb} + \delta^{13}C_{org})(1 - e^{-k\tau})f_{org} \qquad \text{(Equation 5.8)}$$

where M is the amount of buried organic carbon in the Earth's crustal sediments; t is the present age of the sediments deposited at the beginning of an increment of duration τ; and k is the first-order decay constant characteristic of the recycling of the sedimentary environment. For a sediment half-life of 400 million years, $k = (\ln 2)/0.4 = 1.733 \times 10^9\,\text{yr}^{-1}$.

▓ Look at Figure 5.4. Has the quantity of buried organic carbon increased uniformly through time? If not, when did the major changes occur?

▓ The increase has not been uniform. The amount of buried organic carbon increased sharply between about 2.5 billion and 1.8 billion years ago; then it more or less levelled off until about 1.0 billion years ago, when it again increased sharply.

What do these changes in the amount of buried organic carbon tell us about the levels of atmospheric oxygen? We have seen in previous chapters that there is abundant evidence in the rock record for a major change in the atmospheric oxygen levels about 2 billion years ago – for example, BIFs disappeared, red beds appeared, and paleosols became much more oxidized. But what *geological* circumstance could have caused the extra organic carbon burial?

There is no simple answer to this crucial question, but we can make some informed guesses. Let us first consider the state of affairs on the Earth before 2 billion years ago. We know that the first large continental plates began to form roughly between 3 and 2.4 billion years ago. These could have provided environments for sediments to accumulate. We know that large-scale carbonate platforms, with flourishing stromatolite communities, existed then. Although these carbonate platforms contained a lot of organic carbon, studies of modern analogues show that this carbon is so efficiently recycled that only a small proportion gets buried. Thus, it is likely that carbon burial and therefore net oxygen accumulation was low at that time. This is consistent with the low *observed* values of f_{org} in sediments dating from around 2.6–2.4 billion years ago (Figure 5.3). Recall also that there were extensive inorganic sinks for oxygen at that time, for example sea-floor hydrothermal vents supplying reduced iron.

About 2 billion years ago, things changed. By that time, the continental plates had grown, and were beginning to approach their present sizes. This meant that they would also have become large enough to split apart by rifting, in much the same way as Africa and America did about 125 million years ago. There is, in fact, independent evidence for a massive episode of global rifting about 2 billion years ago. Rifting would also have promoted the development of extensive subsiding sedimentary basins, which would have been favourable for the preservation of deposited organic carbon. (A much younger analogue is the North Sea basin, formed as a consequence of the opening up of the Atlantic; the biomass buried by this process eventually became an invaluable source of hydrocarbons – North Sea oil, etc.)

There is another convincing line of evidence for a major geological change about 2 billion years ago: there was a sustained increase in strontium isotope ratios, $^{87}Sr/^{86}Sr$, in seawater at that time (as preserved in marine sediments). (For background information about this, see Box 5.2.)

Box 5.2 Strontium isotopic ratios

Measurement of strontium isotopic ratios in marine sediments provides a means of determining the weathering rates of continental sediments.

The element strontium occurs in nature as several different isotopes. Geochemists are concerned with two of these: ^{86}Sr and ^{87}Sr. The first, ^{86}Sr, is stable and is not the decay product of any other isotope. The other isotope, ^{87}Sr, is produced by the radioactive decay of an isotope of rubidium, ^{87}Rb. Most rocks include strontium *and* rubidium. The strontium in rocks contains both isotopes, ^{87}Sr and ^{86}Sr. However, the radioactive decay of ^{87}Rb to ^{87}Sr in the rock means that the total amount of ^{87}Sr will be continually increasing, whereas ^{86}Sr will remain unchanged. In other words, the ratio $^{87}Sr/^{86}Sr$ will increase with time. In general, rocks that make up the continents have a variable $^{87}Sr/^{86}Sr$ ratio.

The isotopic ratio, $^{87}Sr/^{86}Sr$, in seawater today is constant and is taken to be about 0.7092. This value represents an 'average' of two figures: one (a high value of about 0.7119) derived from rivers that have flowed over the continents into the oceans, and the second (a low value of about 0.7035) from submarine hydrothermal fluids that circulate within the oceanic crust and escape along ocean ridges. This lower value is similar to that of rocks from the upper mantle.

As the present-day strontium isotopic ratio for seawater is constant throughout the world's oceans, any increase in the $^{87}Sr/^{86}Sr$ ratio of seawater indicates an increase in the rate of chemical erosion of the continents.

■   What does an increase in seawater $^{87}Sr/^{86}Sr$ values denote?

■   An increase in the rate of continental weathering, carrying sediments derived from the land, which are characterized by high $^{87}Sr/^{86}Sr$ values, into the oceans.

Increased weathering leads to increased sediment deposition, and therefore increased opportunities for organic carbon burial. There may also have been an early episode of glaciation, which would have lowered sea-levels, thereby promoting sediment erosion. So, overall, the strontium evidence supports the idea of a rise in the amount of buried organic carbon about 2 billion years ago.

During the interval between 1.7 and 1.2 billion years ago, it seems that there was less geological activity, and there is no evidence of glaciation. A relatively stable 'supercontinent' may have existed at that time, with low rates of erosion, sedimentation and organic carbon burial (in part, because there would have been less coastline and less tectonic activity). The rate of carbon burial, and therefore the level of atmospheric oxygen remained steady – at a level higher than existed in the Archean, but still significantly lower than that of today.

During the period between 1.2 and 0.9 billion years ago, geological activity increased again, with episodes of rifting, mountain building and glaciation. The whole pattern of geological activity became more like today's, and the rate of carbon burial increased. As Figure 5.4 shows, a particularly sharp increase in the amount of buried organic carbon after about 1 billion years ago.

▦   What was happening to life on Earth at that period?

▦   As we saw in Chapter 3, during this period animal evolution flourished, leading first to the Ediacaran fauna, and then to the explosive burst of evolution 540 million years ago which defines the beginning of the Phanerozoic period.

This brief study of a complex topic leads us to a crucially important conclusion. The major increases in atmospheric oxygen levels, such as those that occurred about 2 billion years ago and again at about 500 million years ago were not the result of biological innovations, but rather the result of geological changes. Photosynthesis provided a source of oxygen powerful enough to change the world, but the timing and magnitude of oxygen accumulation in the atmosphere were regulated by the internally-driven tectonic processes that controlled erosion and sedimentation. Evolutionary advances were certainly linked to changes in oxygen levels, but the biological changes took place *in response to* atmospheric changes: they did not drive them.

This illuminates one of the most fascinating puzzles in the history of Earth and life. Given that life existed on Earth from almost its earliest days, why did it take billions of years for the first animals to evolve? Animals require efficient aerobic respiration to fuel their metabolism, and this requires oxygen. Oxygen could not accumulate in the atmosphere to useful levels until the large inorganic sinks had been filled, and geological processes had provided the optimum rate of organic carbon burial. Oxygen would, in fact, have been highly toxic to life-forms that had not evolved the appropriate metabolic pathways to cope with it. It has been argued that the process of BIF formation, and the huge sink that it represented, played a useful role by keeping the oxygen at trivial levels for an extended period of time. Life was thus given the opportunity to adapt *gradually* to its own waste product (oxygen), finally learning to harness the process of oxidative degradation of organic matter to meet its own energy requirements.

5.6 Summary of Chapter 5

1   The primary atmosphere of a planet is the one that exists immediately after its formation; the secondary atmosphere is then acquired as the result of subsequent changes.

2   The volatiles that ultimately formed the secondary atmospheres of the terrestrial planets (Mercury, Earth, Venus and Mars) may have arrived in accreted planetary material. Water would have been present chemically bound into the crystal structure of hydrated minerals, or as ice. Carbon and nitrogen would have been present in complex organic compounds, or as methane and ammonia ices. A gaseous molecule can only be retained on a planet if its velocity is less than the planetary escape velocity.

3   Formation of the Earth's secondary atmosphere was driven by its own
        internal differentiation and formation of its core. About 80–85% of the
        Earth's atmosphere was outgassed extremely early in the Earth's history; the
        remainder has been slowly and steadily released over the last 4.4 billion years.
        Outgassing has continued at a more modest rate to the present day through
        volcanoes, which exhale large amounts of water and carbon dioxide.

4   Molecular oxygen on the early (pre-biotic) Earth, could only be formed by
        photolytic dissociation of compounds containing combined oxygen (water
        and carbon dioxide).

5   Once life evolved at the start of the Archean, photosynthesis became the main
        mechanism for oxygen generation. There is evidence of large-scale organic
        carbon burial, but oxygen did not accumulate.

6   At the present day, photosynthetic oxygen generation is balanced by aerobic
        respiration, and atmospheric oxygen can only accumulate through burial of
        organic carbon.

7   In the early Earth, there was no balance between photosynthesis and
        respiration, because huge sinks of ferrous (reduced) iron and volcanic gases
        soaked up photosynthetic oxygen. Methanogenic bacteria also returned large
        amounts of carbon to the atmosphere in the form of methane, which acts as a
        sink for oxygen.

8   There is little evidence for an overall increase in oxygen *production* with time,
        so there must have been a decrease in oxygen *consumption*, perhaps
        ultimately related to the oxidation state of the mantle.

9   Over time, the rate of supply of reduced material to the atmosphere waned,
        while at the same time, geological processes led to increased rates of organic
        carbon burial, permitting atmospheric oxygen levels to rise at the end of the
        Archean and into the Proterozoic. Oxidation of ferrous (reduced) iron supplied
        by deep-ocean hydrothermal vents represented a major sink for oxygen,
        leading to deposition of BIFs, mostly older than about 2 billion years old.

10   Carbon isotope data provide the evidence for the fraction of the total carbon
        which is buried as organic carbon in the sediments, and these data have been
        used to estimate the mass of organic carbon buried during the Proterozoic.
        The rate of carbon burial – and changes in atmospheric oxygen levels – show
        two major increases, one about 2 billion years ago, and the other beginning at
        about 1 billion years ago. Both have been related to changes in geological
        activity – increases in rifting and mountain building – that lead to increased
        burial of sediments.

11   Although *practically all* oxygen in the atmosphere is of biogenic origin,
        increases of atmospheric oxygen levels during the Cryptozoic were dictated
        by inorganic, geological processes. So evolutionary changes in organisms
        followed atmospheric change: they did not drive them.

Now try the following questions to consolidate your understanding of this chapter.

Question 5.3

The abundance of stromatolites on the early Earth suggests that oxygenic
photosynthesizers may have been widespread. The fact that sediments
deposited then contain a fairly constant level of organic carbon (about 0.5%
of their content) means that there must have been a large amount of living
biomass at any one time. But the atmospheric oxygen level does not seem to
have approached its current value until about 500 million years ago. Why did
it not reach higher levels much earlier?

Question 5.4

Measurements of the isotopic composition of carbon in sedimentary rocks 2.5 billion years old show that for carbonate carbon, $\delta^{13}C_{carb}$ averaged 0‰, while for organic carbon, $\delta^{13}C_{org}$ was an average of −45‰ (see Figure 3.9). Use Equation 5.6 to find what fraction of total carbon was therefore being deposited as organic carbon. Remember $\delta^{13}C_{in}$ is −5‰.

Question 5.5

A group of '2.5-billion-year-old sediments contain an average of 0.5% organic carbon. The organic carbon in the sediments represents 0.1% of total carbon'. Expand on these two sentences, and explain how both may be correct – think about the significance of the total carbon.

Question 5.6

The Schidlowski diagram we have used so far (Figure 3.8) suggests that $\delta^{13}C$ for carbonate carbon (C_{carb}) has been relatively unchanged over geological time. During 1996, while this book was being edited, a paper appeared in the American journal *Science* demonstrating that there was a well-defined increase in $\delta^{13}C$ for carbonate carbon between 2.2 and 2 billion years ago, with values of $\delta^{13}C$ reaching +10‰. Comment on this finding in terms of biological processes, oxygen production, and the inferences to be drawn from Figure 5.3, which was based on earlier data.

Chapter 6
Modelling the evolution of atmospheric oxygen levels during the Phanerozoic

6.1 Introduction

So far we have used indirect evidence, such as the Earth's fossil and rock records, to deduce the likely levels of oxygen in the atmosphere over geological time (Chapters 3 and 4). In Chapter 5, we set about interpreting the early oxygen levels in terms of the underlying processes operating during the Cryptozoic – from the beginning of the Earth until about 540 million years ago.

We now continue the story through the Phanerozoic, from about 540 million years ago to the present day, by examining how the oxygen level evolved and some of its implications. But this time we use a different approach – that of modelling. We shall, in fact, focus on one specific model, that devised by Berner and Canfield (Sections 6.3 and 6.4). We end the chapter with a brief look at the effects that elevated oxygen levels predicted by the Berner and Canfield model might have had on life during the late Paleozoic (Section 6.5).

6.2 Using models

Scientists construct hypotheses to describe how the world works. They attempt to test these hypotheses by making predictions based on them, and then confirming, modifying or rejecting those predictions by carrying out experiments. In this way, hypotheses are established, modified or discarded. Because it is difficult to carry out experiments in the Earth System, scientists are obliged to construct models of how they think the world works (see Box 6.1). Weather forecasters can test their models by making forecasts two or three days ahead, and then waiting to see what the weather is like. Climate modellers, working with time-scales of thousands or millions of years have more difficult problems. One approach they employ is 'retrodiction' – using their model of the climate system to infer what conditions would have been like at some specific point in the past, and then checking this prediction against the evidence preserved in the rock record.

Atmospheric scientists use the same approach, for example in studying the Phanerozoic atmosphere. There is strong evidence from the fossil record that oxygen levels during the Phanerozoic were between about 15 and 30% (Chapter 3). Two American scientists, Robert Berner and Donald Canfield, have used modelling to attempt to refine these rather vague limits. Like most models, that of Berner and Canfield is a simplification of the much more complicated real world in which a prodigious number of interrelated factors interact to determine the level of atmospheric oxygen, making it difficult to unravel what is going on. The model substitutes things that can be measured (or which we think can be measured) for things that cannot. It also simplifies the actual processes involved – since we are only interested in *outcomes*, detailed understanding of all the intermediate steps is unnecessary.

Box 6.1 More about models

A model is a representation of some part of our world. Models can be physical objects: a scale model of a car or building, or a museum model of a dinosaur that has been constructed by informed guesswork of how flesh lay on fossil bones. Models can also be mental constructs: a 'model' holiday, for instance, denoting some abstract representation of the perfect vacation. At a more practical level, a model can be a representation of a highly complex object, such as the model of the Earth as a layered structure (Figure 1.1). Numerical or mathematical models are, in principle, no different. Scientists develop them as abstract simplifications of the behaviour or processes that are under study. As one scientist put it, 'Science is the art of finding the simplest rules to explain the prodigious jumble of the world.'

One type of model involves linking changes in one parameter to changes in another, more easily measurable process. It may not even be necessary to know why the parameters are linked (although this helps to inspire confidence in the predictions of the model), but only that such a link exists. These models are termed *empirical models*. Foresters, for example, may determine that, for any given species of tree, there is a strong correlation between the diameter of a tree trunk and the amount of usable wood it yields. They can then estimate the anticipated yield from an entire plantation of different sized trees by simply measuring the diameter of the trunks, without any need to understand how trees grow.

Other models, the so-called *process-based models*, require some understanding of the processes controlling the phenomenon of interest. Consider the problems faced by a water company that owns a single water reservoir with capacity x (in m^3). If the company's customers are thought likely to consume water at a rate of y (in m^3 per day), and if rainfall replenishes the reservoir at z (in m^3 per day), then the company could predict that the reservoir would run dry in: $x/(y - z)$ days. More refined models would include, among other things, estimates of how the rate of consumption varies with temperature, and how the rate of replenishment would be affected by evaporation in hot weather. But even the simple model would yield predictions that could be tested.

The choice of model depends on both the purpose and the resources available. For instance, if one is not too interested in examining the controlling factors, or one does not have the evidence to reconstruct the mechanisms, an empirical model is useful. On the other hand, if one is specifically interested in testing hypotheses about how a particular phenomenon is controlled, then a process-based model may be called for.

Regardless of the type, independent evidence may be used to strengthen, modify or, in some cases, even refute any particular model.

6.3 The Berner and Canfield model

We do not have space to explore Berner and Canfield's work in full, but it is useful to understand their approach and their conclusions. They developed their model on the premise that the level of atmospheric oxygen at any one time during the Phanerozoic was dictated by the balance between the rate of sediment deposition and burial, and the rate of sediment erosion (i.e. weathering).

Berner and Canfield reduced the whole Earth System to a single equation which can be expressed as:

$$R_O = F_{BC} + \frac{15}{8} F_{BS} - \left(F_{WC} + \frac{15}{8} F_{WS} \right)$$
(Equation 6.1)

where the variables are defined as follows:

R_O = rate of change in oxygen level with time (if the rate is positive the oxygen level is increasing, if it is negative the level is decreasing)

F_{BC} = world burial rate of organic carbon in sediments

F_{BS} = world burial rate of sulfur contained in pyrite

F_{WC} = world weathering rate of carbon in organic-carbon bearing sediments

F_{WS} = world weathering rate of pyrite

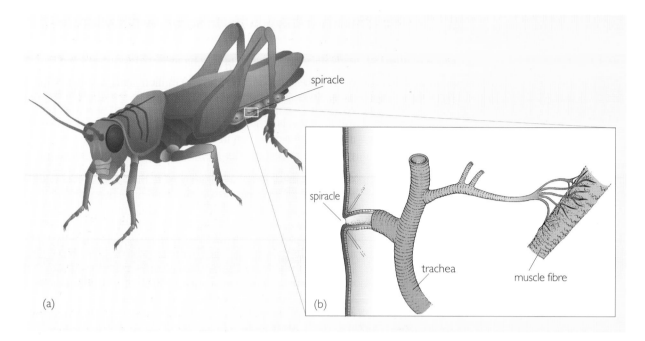

(a)

(b)

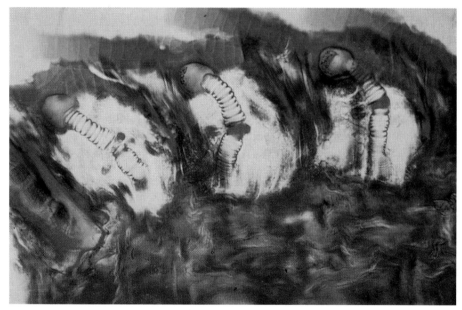

(c)

Figure 6.2
(a) Spiracles along the abdomen of a locust.
(b) Spiracles and trachea provide routes for atmospheric oxygen to diffuse into a locust's muscle tissue. Therefore, the muscle is aerated by direct contact with the air, rather than by the circulation of blood.
(c) A cross-section through the abdomen of an insect showing trachea.

However, if you stop breathing, and simply sit with your mouth open, you will rapidly discover the limitations of respiration by diffusion. Not nearly enough oxygen will diffuse into your lungs, and you will soon be gasping for breath. Organisms that respire by diffusion therefore require a high surface area in relation to their volume in order to accommodate a sufficient number of spiracles.

■   This imposes a limit on the size of such organisms. Why?

■   As the volume of their body increases, so the relative surface area through which they can respire decreases.

In theory, the surface area per unit volume in organisms could be maximized by their having paper-thin bodyplans. This is exactly what happens in plants, which respire by diffusion through the holes in their leaves called *stomata*. But paper-thin animals would be at a disadvantage in many obvious ways.

Calculations based on the physics of diffusion show that at the present-day level of oxygen, the maximum functional length of trachea connecting the muscle to the atmosphere is about 1.2 mm: if the trachea were any longer, oxygen could not diffuse along it fast enough to supply the needs of the muscles. This sets a firm limit to the size of diffusion-respiring organisms. Observation and experience confirm that there are no really large flying insects around today – even the largest beetles are only a few centimetres across.

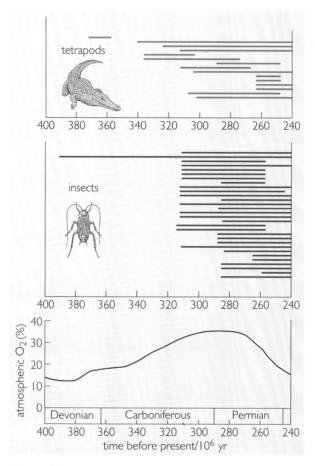

Figure 6.3
The lower graph illustrates the elevated atmospheric oxygen levels (the Paleozoic oxygen peak) between about 340 and 250 million years ago. The upper two plots indicate the appearance and disappearance of various insects and tetrapods. The rise and fall in oxygen levels has been linked to, first, the evolution and, then to the extinction of many kinds of insects and other animals. Up to 30% of insect orders may have become extinct at the end of the Permian (at about 245 million years ago).

Respiration by diffusion, however, is such an extremely simple and effective process in small animals that it evolved separately several times in terrestrial invertebrates: in insects, spiders, and crustaceans (such as wood-lice), as well as in worms and vascular plants such as trees and shrubs. At higher atmospheric oxygen levels, longer trachea and hence larger bodies would be possible. One estimate suggests that in an atmosphere containing 35% oxygen (the predicted oxygen peak at about 280 million years ago), the largest diffusion-respiring organism could have been 27% bigger than those found in today's atmosphere.

A possible increase in the size of worms in the Paleozoic might appear to be of limited interest. But there are other possibilities – the combination of an increased atmospheric density and enriched oxygen level *may* have contributed to the development of flying insects, and so to the huge new radiation of different insect species that flight made possible. We know from the fossil record that flying insects first emerged about 300 million years ago and that flight became the decisive agent of the rapid dispersal and diversification of insects through the Carboniferous (Figure 6.3).

It is possible that the earliest 'proto-wings' were used for thermoregulation and also for respiration, providing an increased surface area for oxygen diffusion, and that their use for locomotion and escape was secondary. However, an increased atmospheric density would have favoured flight – few modern helicopters can fly at heights above 4000 m, since the air is too thin, and they fly best close to sea-level. By analogy, for insects the aerodynamic lift generated by even rudimentary primitive wings could become significant at elevated atmospheric densities.

A higher level of atmospheric oxygen would also have had a less obvious side effect. Just as a helicopter has to use prodigious amounts of air and fuel to stay airborne, so too do insects. A flying insect 'burns up' a lot of oxygen – about 6.5 moles per cubic metre of muscle tissue per second. Therefore flying insects require a very effective oxidative metabolism to 'burn' (oxidize) their fuel. In the absence of changes to their metabolic processes, increasing atmospheric oxygen levels would have helped them to do this. It also meant that flying insects could have been *larger*.

■　　How big are the largest flying insects today?

■　　The largest butterflies, locusts and dragonflies have wingspans of 10–20 cm, but their soft body parts are never thicker than a human finger.

Fossil dragonflies are well known from the geological record. Those that lived in the Carboniferous, during the peak in oxygen levels, reached startling dimensions, with wingspans of up to 70 cm. *Meganeura monyi* a giant dragonfly, had a body almost 3 cm in diameter, far larger than modern dragonflies (Figure 6.4). Significantly, at the end of the Permian (about 245 million years ago), when, according to the Berner and Canfield model, oxygen levels had decreased, 27–30% of all known insect orders were lost, including the giant dragonflies. So both the sudden increase and development of insect life and its subsequent decline are in keeping with a peak in the level of atmospheric oxygen followed by a decline – as predicted by the Berner and Canfield model. However, we should not lose sight of the fact that other factors may have come into play.

Question 6.2
You will often have seen small dragonflies skimming across the surface of modern ponds in pursuit of their food. What sort of animals pursue modern dragonflies for food? Comment on this in relation to the large sizes of dragonflies 300 million years ago.

(a)

(b)

Figure 6.4
(a) A fossil specimen of the giant dragonfly, *Meganeura monyi*. Outlines of the two sets of wings are clearly visible, together with traces of their characteristic vein structure, particularly near the centre. Traces of the insect's body can be seen at an oblique angle to the deep groove in the rock. (b) A reconstruction of the dragonfly alive: it resembles its modern counterparts, although it was several times bigger.

Elevated oxygen levels could also have affected marine life. Diffusion of oxygen through water is far less efficient than through air, so most marine organisms evolved mechanisms for pumping water through their bodies. Although many factors besides oxygen levels may have been involved in the development of this mechanism, there was a striking increase in the size of many marine invertebrates, such as corals, foraminfera and brachiopods, during the period of elevated atmospheric oxygen. An example that is common in the Carboniferous limestone deposits of the north of England is the huge brachiopod *Gigantoproductus*, with a shell reaching up to 30 cm across.

Terrestrial vertebrates would have also been affected by increasing atmospheric oxygen. In fact, it may have enabled them to crawl on to land from the sea 300 million years ago. For us highly-evolved vertebrates, breathing air still has one disadvantage: it caused us to dry out. As the mist that condenses on a mirror confirms, every time we breathe out, we lose some water by evaporation from our lungs. For early vertebrates, equipped with both gills and only inefficient primitive lungs, this problem was acute – they would have to take more breaths. If the air contained more oxygen, then an animal would need to breathe proportionately less of it, and so would lose less water. Thus, elevated oxygen levels may have facilitated the evolution of air-breathing animals.

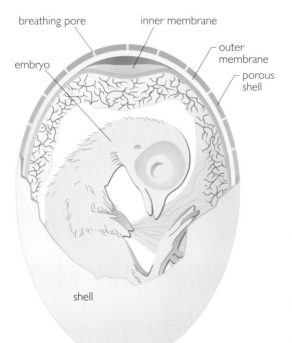

breathing pore   inner membrane

outer membrane

porous shell

embryo

shell

Gills work well in water, as the existence of fishes amply demonstrates. But they work much less well in air, primarily because gills are not effective at liberating carbon dioxide – a process that is just as important for metabolism as taking up oxygen from the air. Therefore, elevated atmospheric oxygen levels, coupled with a reduction in carbon dioxide (as mentioned in Section 6.4), would have enhanced the effectiveness of primitive lungs and thus encouraged their evolutionary success.

The evolutionary progression of vertebrates from fish to amphibians, then to reptiles and on to mammals is a familiar one, and we shall not dwell on it here. One vital step, however, may have been permitted by the increase in atmospheric oxygen levels during the late Paleozoic: the evolution of reptiles from amphibians, which enabled animals to colonize the land. Perhaps the most important difference between amphibians and reptiles is that reproduction of the latter is via the amniotic egg, of which the chicken egg is an example.

An egg forms a capsule, in which the embryo can grow to a state such that the newborn can fend for itself more or less from the moment of hatching. Amphibian eggs have no shell; only a thin permeable membrane through which gases diffuse. Hence, they have to be laid in water – on land, they would rapidly desiccate. Amniotic eggs have a marvellous anatomy (Figure 6.5). The egg is enclosed in a mineralized shell, which is the focus of our attention since it provides the interface between the atmosphere and the interior of the egg (in effect, the embryo itself). An eggshell has to be strong enough to protect the embryo, but not so strong that the newborn cannot break out. It also has to be sufficiently porous to enable oxygen to diffuse into the interior and for waste gases to exit. If you examine your breakfast boiled egg before tackling it (big end or little end?), you will note that the shell is perforated with pores through which the gases diffuse.

Figure 6.5
Anatomy of a modern egg. Oxygen diffuses through the porous shell and the permeable membrane (both inner and outer) and keeps the chick embryo alive.

■   What effect might increasing atmospheric oxygen levels have on the spacing of pores in the shell?

■   They could be further apart, since fewer pores would be needed to supply the same amount of oxygen.

If the pores remained the same size, fewer pores would mean the shell would be stronger, providing more protection for the embryo within; alternatively larger eggs with the same thickness (and strength) shell could exist. However, if the pore spacing remained the same at higher oxygen levels, then the shell could be thicker and stronger, and the longer diffusion path would be off-set by the greater oxygen concentration. Overall, then, increasing atmospheric oxygen levels would have been advantageous for the evolution of reptile eggs, enabling animals to move away from water for the first time and to thus 'conquer the land'.

Thus, the independent evidence contained in the fossil record is consistent with a peak in atmospheric oxygen levels during the late Paleozoic – as predicted by the Berner and Canfield model.

6.6 Summary of Chapter 6

1   Berner and Canfield modelled levels of atmospheric oxygen over the Phanerozoic by considering the burial rates of pyrite and organic carbon, compared with the weathering rates of pyrite and carbon-bearing sediments. They concluded that the mean atmospheric oxygen level had remained between 15 and 35% over the last 540 million years.

2   The Berner and Canfield model predicts a large peak in atmospheric oxygen levels between about 350 and 250 million years ago, when the level may have reached a maximum of 35% (1.7 PAL). They ascribed this peak to the evolution of woody plants containing lignin, and also to the existence of a large supercontinent (Pangea) with extensive sedimentary basins, both of which may have promoted enhanced rates of organic carbon burial.

3   Elevated atmospheric oxygen levels during the late Paleozoic would have led to:
   ◆   a higher atmospheric density, as the oxygen would have been an addition to the atmosphere, and there is no ready mechanism for removing nitrogen;
   ◆   an increase in the size (by about 27% for the peak oxygen level) of organisms which respire by diffusion through their body walls via trachea;
   ◆   an increase in dissolved oxygen, which could in turn have led to a higher marine biomass.

4   Elevated atmospheric density and oxygen content may have promoted the evolution of flying insects such as dragonflies, which attained their largest dimensions during the period of the postulated oxygen peak. Elevated oxygen levels would also have encouraged the development of lungs rather than gills and the laying of eggs on land by reptiles, and thus the 'conquest of the land' by animals.

Now try the following questions to consolidate your understanding of this chapter.

Question 6.3
If the Earth's atmosphere consisted of 21% carbon dioxide and 79% nitrogen, would you expect the atmospheric density at the surface of the Earth to be similar to that found today? If not, would it be higher or lower? (A qualitative answer is all that is required.)

Question 6.4
Modern flying birds reach far bigger sizes than the giant dragonflies of the Carboniferous, although today's atmospheric density is lower than that suggested by modelling work? Can you explain this?

Table 8.1 Absorption cross-sections of molecular oxygen and ozone at four wavelengths.

Wavelength of light/μm	Absorption cross-section/cm²	
	O_2	O_3
0.150	1×10^{-17}	–
0.200	1×10^{-23}	1×10^{-18}
0.250	2×10^{-25}	1×10^{-17}
0.300	–	1×10^{-18}

▨ What part of the electromagnetic spectrum do the data in Table 8.1 refer to?

▨ The wavelengths are all in the ultraviolet region (recall that visible light has wavelengths between 0.4 and 0.7 μm).

▨ Which gas is the better absorber at (a) 0.150 μm, and (b) 0.250 μm?

▨ Oxygen is the better absorber at 0.150 μm, and ozone at 0.250 μm.

Table 8.1 shows that at *very* short ultraviolet wavelengths, molecular oxygen is a highly effective absorber. Its efficiency falls off rapidly, however, at longer wavelengths, whereas ozone is most effective between 0.2 and 0.3 μm. So, the two forms of oxygen share the job of preventing harmful short-wavelength radiation from reaching the Earth's surface: most of this short-wavelength radiation is absorbed above 100 km altitude in the atmosphere.

Of course, the effectiveness of a gas as an absorber in the atmosphere depends not only on its absorption cross-section, but also on its abundance.

▨ As you know, 21% of the atmosphere is oxygen and only about 5×10^{-6}% is ozone. Other factors being equal, which gas in the atmosphere absorbs more radiation at 0.200 μm?

▨ At 0.200 μm, ozone molecules are $10^{-18}/10^{-23}$ as effective as oxygen, or 1×10^5 times more effective, so one ozone molecule is 'worth' 1×10^5 oxygen molecules. But oxygen is $21/(5 \times 10^{-6})$, or 4.2×10^6 times more abundant than ozone. Overall, therefore, oxygen is $(4.2 \times 10^6/10^5)$ or 42 times more effective as an absorber of radiation of wavelength 0.200 μm than ozone.

The changing effects of oxygen and ozone are best summarized graphically (Figure 8.2). This shows how effectively the mixture of gases in the *modern* atmosphere prevents ultraviolet radiation from reaching surface levels. Of course, oxygen (and therefore ozone) were effectively absent from the Earth's early atmosphere. Let us explore the effects of lower atmospheric oxygen levels, and by implication, ozone, by examining a modern phenomenon: the ozone hole. This results from the destruction of ozone in the stratosphere by chlorofluorocarbons (CFCs) in high-latitude regions: in satellite maps of ozone distribution, there appears to be a hole centred over the South Pole (Figure 8.3).

Figure 8.2
The depth of penetration of solar radiation into the Earth's atmosphere as a function of wavelength, and the principal absorbing gases. Both oxygen and ozone are important absorbers of ultraviolet radiation. Only at wavelengths longer than about 0.300 μm does sunlight reach the Earth's surface at *full* intensity. (This is a schematic diagram which is not representative of the whole Earth at all times. Some radiation between 0.200 and 0.300 μm does reach the surface during the day.)

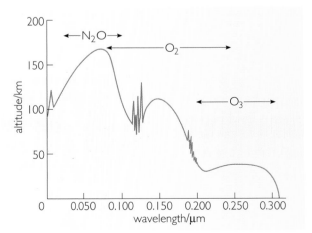

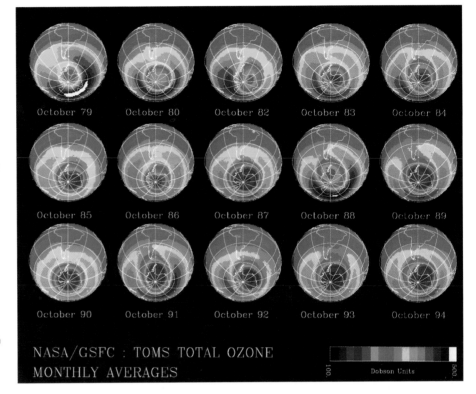

Figure 8.3
Satellite views over the South Pole each October from 1979 to 1994, showing the increasing size of the ozone hole, resulting from diffusion of artificial CFCs into the stratosphere. These images are from the Total Ozone Mapping Spectrometer (TOMS) on board NASA's Nimbus 7 Satellite. They are given in Dobson Units (DU) which is a measure of the amount of ozone in a column of atmosphere. I DU is equivalent to 2.7×10^{16} molecules cm^{-2}.

Figure 8.4 shows the observed variation in average winter and summer daily ultraviolet flux with time over Toronto, Canada since 1989, while Figure 8.5 shows in more detail the variation in the ozone absorption cross-section with wavelength. (Note that the average daily flux at $0.300\,\mu m$ is about 100 times lower than at $0.324\,\mu m$ – as you would expect from the information in Figures 8.2 and 8.5.) Study Figure 8.4 and then answer the following question.

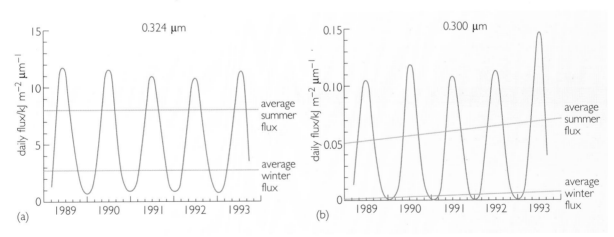

Figure 8.4
Daily total integrated ultraviolet flux at (a) $0.324\,\mu m$ and (b) $0.300\,\mu m$ measured at Toronto, Canada between 1989 and 1993. The straight lines indicate the average summer and average winter flux values, eliminating the annual cycle. (Note the units of flux used: $kJ\,m^{-2}\,\mu m^{-1}$; kilojoules per square metre per micrometre; or energy per unit area per unit wavelength.) (Reprinted with permission from Kerr, J. B. and McElroy, C. T. 'Evidence for large upward trends of ultraviolet-B radiation linked to ozone depletion', *Science*, **262**, 12 November 1993. Copyright 1993 American Association for the Advancement of Science.)

Chapter 9
Carbon dioxide and the Earth

9.1 Introduction

In the first part of this book, we traced the evolution of atmospheric oxygen by using clues in the fossil and rock records. We now turn to an equally important atmospheric constituent for life: atmospheric carbon dioxide. In many ways the two gases have danced a complementary duet: periods of major changes in atmospheric oxygen levels over the Earth's history also coincide with large changes in atmospheric carbon dioxide levels. A 17th century Belgian chemist, Jan Baptist van Helmont, was the first to identify carbon dioxide as a gas distinct from others, and to realize that it was a product of both fermentation and combustion.

Anyone who has stood for too long in a crowded lift or a popular nightclub and has felt the need for a 'breath of fresh air' appreciates the importance of oxygen. It is more difficult to appreciate the importance of carbon dioxide for life. But consider this: plants *must* have carbon dioxide for photosynthesis. Without carbon dioxide there would be no green plants. And without plants, there would be no atmospheric oxygen and no higher life-forms. Therefore, the two gases, oxygen and carbon dioxide, are intimately connected. Aerobic life (including all of us) survives by regulating chemical reactions involving the two.

There is an additional feature of atmospheric carbon dioxide that makes it essential for life on this planet: its role in regulating surface temperature, and therefore climate. Through the greenhouse effect, carbon dioxide absorbs outgoing infrared radiation and re-radiates it in the atmosphere, so warming the Earth. Without some carbon dioxide in the atmosphere the Earth would be frozen. But could we ever have too much of a good thing?

9.2 Divergent paths

In Section 5.2, we briefly discussed the origins of the earliest atmospheres of the four terrestrial planets. It is clear that while the atmospheres of Mercury, Venus, Earth and Mars all had similar beginnings, they evolved in dramatically different ways. Table 9.1 compares some physical and chemical properties of the Earth and its 'sister planet' Venus. By inspection of their physical attributes, you can see that the siblings are quite similar in diameter, mass and density, and both contain about the same amount of total carbon. However, when you look at where that carbon is distributed, it begins to look as though Earth has a sister from hell. With over 96% of its carbon present as carbon dioxide in the atmosphere, the atmospheric pressure on Venus is a crushing 93 times that of the Earth, and its surface temperature is a decidedly uncomfortable 460 °C. If life ever existed on Venus, it has long since been annihilated.

Section 5.2 hinted at the possible reasons the planets took such different courses. Since it is closer to the Sun, and therefore receives more intense solar energy, practically all the water in the early Venusian atmosphere has been lost through photolytic dissociation. Venus evolved to be hot and dry (Figure 9.1); Earth is warm and wet.

Table 9.1 Comparison of Venus and the Earth.

	Venus	Earth
diameter/km	12 100	12 756
mass/10^{24} kg	4.9	6.0
density/kg m^{-3}	5.24×10^3	5.52×10^3
distance from Sun/10^6 km	108	150
total carbon/kg	10^{20}	10^{20}*
atmospheric CO_2 (vol %)	96.5%	0.036%†
surface temperature/°C	460	15
surface pressure/terrestrial bars	93	1
column mass/kg m^{-2}	1.03×10^6	1.03×10^4
total atmospheric mass/kg	4.74×10^{20}	5.3×10^{18}

*This is a rather uncertain value and does not include any carbon that may be present in the mantle.

†This is the 1996 value. Because the concentration is steadily increasing, you may encounter different values elsewhere, depending on the date and source of the reference.

Figure 9.1
Venus as seen in an ultraviolet image taken by the spaceprobe Pioneer 12 on 11 February 1979. The clouds, which are composed of tiny droplets of sulfuric acid, cover the planet entirely. The atmosphere, nearly all carbon dioxide, exerts a surface pressure 93 times that of the Earth's atmosphere.

Chapter 10 introduces the first model, which exploits established correlations between carbon dioxide concentrations and temperature to reconstruct levels of atmospheric carbon dioxide over the entire history of the Earth. This empirical model combines basic principles of energy balance and stellar evolution with atmospheric physics and chemistry, and relies little on environmental clues left by nature, of which there are precious few for the early Earth. It can give us broad limits on *how* the level of atmospheric carbon dioxide has changed over geological time, but it cannot tell us *why* it has changed.

The second model, discussed in Chapter 11, is more complicated but, as a result, more powerful. This process-based model builds mathematical representations of the major processes that we believe release and consume atmospheric carbon dioxide, and of how the rates of these processes change over time. In contrast to the first approach, it relies heavily on the available evidence of environmental conditions on the Earth, and so requires a continuous record of fossil and geological evidence. In both Chapters 10 and 11 we shall evaluate the assumptions and evidence for the model presented, and discuss the implications for life on Earth.

Finally in Chapter 12, we shall consider an overview of the evolution over geological time of the two atmospheric constituents that are both vital for life and profoundly affected by life: oxygen and carbon dioxide. By understanding how the atmosphere has changed over time as reflected in these two gases, we hope that you will be able to see our modern Atmosphere–Earth–Life System as part of a long continuum stretching back to the origin of the Earth itself, one in which all three components have always been inextricably linked.

9.4 Summary of Chapter 9

1   Water has played a vital role in keeping the Earth habitable as it helps to remove carbon dioxide from the atmosphere, thus avoiding a runaway greenhouse effect.

2   Most of the carbon in the Earth's crust is locked away within the rocks and sediments.

3   We must rely on models to reconstruct how atmospheric CO_2 has changed over the Earth's history.

Chapter 10
An empirical model of atmospheric carbon dioxide levels during the Cryptozoic

10.1 Introduction

We have an ambitious goal: to reconstruct the level of atmospheric CO_2 over the whole of the Earth's existence. This is an exceptionally tall order, considering there is essentially no evidence of conditions on Earth for the first 600 million years, and precious little for billions of years thereafter. Nevertheless, in this chapter we shall discuss one way atmospheric CO_2 may be broadly estimated for the Cryptozoic Eon.

As you already know, the Earth's history is divided into two eons: the Cryptozoic (also called the Precambrian) from 4.6 billion years ago to about 540 million years ago, and the Phanerozoic, from 540 million years ago to the present day. The Cryptozoic Eon itself is divided into three eras: the Hadean, the Archean and the Proterozoic. We can tell a bit more about each successive era both because the Earth becomes more similar to contemporary conditions, and because less evidence has been destroyed by geological processes. But any model of CO_2 covering the Cryptozoic must necessarily rely on fairly simple assumptions and require little hard data. So first we must assemble what we *do* know and then collect together the available data, and examine how they can be used as tools for our model.

We set the stage in Section 10.2 with five propositions about what the Earth was like over the early Cryptozoic (during the Hadean). In Section 10.3 we use our knowledge of carbon chemistry to estimate the *maximum* atmospheric CO_2 level at the Earth's very beginning. In Section 10.4 we estimate the *minimum* atmospheric CO_2 level for that time by using basic principles of global energy balance. In the remaining sections, Sections 10.5–10.8, we shall reconstruct the change in atmospheric CO_2 over the whole of the Cryptozoic from this earliest level using an empirical model.

10.2 Some propositions about the Hadean Earth

Despite there being little direct evidence, we can use indirect evidence to construct a picture of what the Earth was like during the Hadean. We can outline a series of 'propositions' to set some limits on atmospheric CO_2 even this far back in time.

Proposition 1: More than 4 billion years ago, the early Earth was hotter and geologically more active than today

There is every reason to suppose that the Hadean lived up to its name. The Earth's surface was periodically bombarded by asteroids and comets, and baked by subterranean heat arising from the decay of radioactive isotopes, core formation and primordial heat left over from accretion. Large amounts of energy were liberated, which resulted in rapid convective overturn of the mantle and intensely active volcanism.

Proposition 2: Carbon existed in the early atmosphere primarily as CO_2

As you saw in Section 5.2.2, current thinking is that the Earth's secondary atmosphere formed rapidly at the end of the major period of accretion (which lasted about 150 million years). Some gases (including water vapour) were trapped in the accreted material that formed the body of the Earth and were later outgassed from the interior to the surface, while other gases arrived through continuing impacts of volatile-rich cometary material. The iron-rich core was formed by the heavier elements segregating from the lighter and sinking to the Earth's centre.

The oxidation state of the early atmosphere would determine whether atmospheric carbon existed primarily as carbon dioxide or as methane. Early formation of the core played a vital role, because it removed elemental iron (a strong reducing agent) from contact with the gasses emanating from the mantle and escaping into the atmosphere. It is likely, then, that the Earth's early atmosphere was not *strongly* reduced. A strongly reduced atmosphere would have been dominated by gases such as ammonia (NH_3) and methane (CH_4). Instead, it was probably *weakly* reduced, dominated by N_2 and CO_2. However, depending on the oxidation state of the early mantle (still a matter of debate), the atmosphere could have contained a substantial amount of carbon in the form of carbon monoxide (CO; which is less oxidized than CO_2) and even some methane. There is debate over whether the mantle was fully oxidized upon formation of the core some 4.5 billion years ago, or if the mantle was weakly reduced and became progressively more oxidized over time (Section 4.4). For now we must leave this as unresolved.

Proposition 3: Rain removed a substantial amount of CO_2 from the atmosphere to the oceans at some point in the Hadean, probably the early Hadean

In addition to the differentiation of the core, a further critical event in Hadean was the formation of the oceans. During the period of accretion when the surface of the Earth was subjected to intense heat from continued bombardment, water would have existed as steam in the atmosphere. Some of this water would have come from volcanic outgassing, some would have arrived from comets. In any case, at some point in the post-accretionary phase the Earth's surface would have cooled sufficiently for water vapour in the atmosphere to precipitate as rain to form the oceans. Because CO_2 is so soluble in water, the rain would transfer a substantial amount of the CO_2 from the atmosphere to the oceans. We don't know when this happened, but it was certainly before 3.8 billion years ago (the age of the oldest rock formations known, which include pillow lavas deposited under water – discussed further in Section 10.5) and probably much earlier.

Proposition 4: There were few or no continents during the early Hadean

Continental crust is manufactured from mantle rocks via complex geological cycles which take considerable lengths of time. The oldest known rocks are about 3.8–4 billion years old. Strontium isotopes preserved in carbonates (Section 5.4) suggest that land-based weathering has influenced seawater composition for at least the last 3 billion years. Weathering must have occurred before this, for time was required for continental land masses to grow sufficiently large to influence the strontium isotopic ratio of seawater. However, there is no evidence for any sizeable continents being present during the earliest period in the Earth's history. This is important because continental land provides a long-term storage for the major inorganic carbon sink – carbonate rock.

Proposition 5: The total amount of carbon on the Earth has not greatly changed since its formation

There is no easy way for carbon to leave the Earth in large quantities. Whereas light gases such as hydrogen and helium could escape to space, CO_2 is too heavy to achieve its escape velocity (Section 5.2.2). Some carbon would, in fact, be *gained* by the Earth through the arrival of carbonaceous chondrites (carbon-containing meteorites), but this would be negligible in comparison to the amount already contained within the Earth.

10.3 Setting some limits for the Hadean: the maximum atmospheric CO_2 level

The Earth of 4 billion years ago almost certainly presented a different appearance from space than it does today. It was probably enveloped in clouds, covered by water, pockmarked with acid-belching volcanoes, and bombarded by impacts. Despite that, our planet was in all likelihood already capable of sustaining life. This is largely due to two things – the presence of liquid water, and the removal of a substantial amount of atmospheric carbon dioxide, thus avoiding a runaway greenhouse effect.

If we accept the propositions put forward above, we can use that information to estimate how much CO_2 was removed from the atmosphere. To begin with, we might ask 'what is the maximum amount of CO_2 that could have been present in the atmosphere during the Hadean?'

We shall start by looking at the crust. There are about 10^{20} kg of carbon on the Earth's surface today contained in the crustal rocks, sediments, soils, ocean, atmosphere and biosphere (and an unknown amount in the mantle and core). Let us assume that, to a first approximation, the same amount of carbon was present on the Earth's surface 4.5 billion years ago. Effectively, this means that we assume there has been no significant net transfer of carbon from the mantle to the crust or vice versa over time.

At around 4.5 billion years ago then, the warm, water-covered Earth contained a total of about 10^{20} kg of carbon on its surface (including the crust). Since continents did not yet exist, the major carbon store today (carbonate rocks on land) also did not exist. So, very much more carbon must have been partitioned between the atmosphere, the ocean, and the primitive sea floor 4.5 billion years ago than is today. Thus, if we could determine the distribution of carbon among these three reservoirs, we could then estimate the proportion of total carbon that was in the atmosphere, and in turn the level of atmospheric CO_2 at the Earth's beginning. Let us see if that is possible.

Partitioning carbon between the atmosphere and the ocean *alone* would be a relatively straightforward exercise, complicated only by the dependence of CO_2 solubility on temperature and water chemistry – and therefore guesses we would need to make about the composition of the early ocean. However, the presence of sea-floor sediments makes things more complicated. Depending on their chemical and physical compositions and that of the surrounding water, such sediments could be a large sink of carbon, a small sink, or none at all. At one extreme, if the sea-floor sediments could not be considered as a sink for any carbon at all, the Earth's carbon would be partitioned entirely between the atmosphere and the ocean. Thus, we must try to pin down the composition of the early sea floor.

It is probably safe to say that the level of dissolved inorganic carbon in the early ocean was considerably higher than it is today. Also, because the early heat flux of the Earth was much higher than the present day, Earth was probably geologically far more active, with more hydrothermal activity on mid-ocean ridges. The American geochemist James Walker has argued that these are precisely the conditions that could allow the formation of **carbonated basalts** on the sea floor (Figure 10.1).

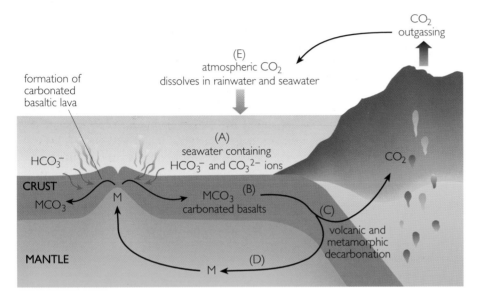

Figure 10.1
Presumed geochemical carbon cycle of the early Earth (during the Hadean). (A) Seawater containing bicarbonate and carbonate ions flows through the cracks and fissures in the sides of hydrothermal vents. The dissolved inorganic carbon is removed from seawater by carbonation reactions in hydrothermal vents. (B) Carbon is stored on the sea floor as carbonated basalt, represented as MCO_3. 'M' refers to metal ions such as calcium, magnesium and iron. (C) Carbon is released as CO_2 from sea-floor carbonates through volcanic and metamorphic decarbonation reactions followed by outgassing. (D) The metal ions are recycled through the mantle. (E) Atmospheric CO_2 is re-dissolved into the ocean in equilibrium with seawater. (Note this figure is not to scale.)

Carbonated basalts are basalts containing calcium-, magnesium-, and iron carbonates. They can form in hydrothermal vents when seawater is drawn in through the sides of the vents toward the hot centres by hydrothermal convection. There, seawater is heated by contact with molten basalt lava. Now, if the vents are deep enough below the ocean surface, the pressure will be sufficient to prevent escape of CO_2 in bubbles. If the level of dissolved inorganic carbon is high enough, calcium-, magnesium-, and iron carbonates will be deposited, thus sequestering the carbon from seawater. Such carbonated basalts would then comprise the primordial sea floor.

Although known Archean rocks do seem to have a higher proportion of carbonated basalts than more-recently formed rocks, these could have been carbonated by subsequent metamorphism or other alteration much later – their existence does not *in itself* prove or disprove the hypothesis. However, if we accept the proposition that carbonation reactions could have been important in the early ocean, we have a potentially significant sink for atmospheric CO_2. How important a sink is the next question we must answer.

Walker argues that the high level of dissolved inorganic carbon in early seawater (see Proposition 3) would have set up a highly efficient carbonation system, removing nearly all of the dissolved inorganic carbon from the seawater drawn into hydrothermal vents. (This process is insignificant today because of the lower concentration of dissolved inorganic carbon in the seawater.) So let us *postulate* a perfectly efficient sink: any seawater drawn into a vent has all its carbon removed and deposited in solid form as carbonate.

Carbonated sediments do not accumulate forever, but are cycled back into the mantle by tectonic processes. To estimate the total amount of inorganic carbon stored on the sea floor, we need to estimate the rate at which dissolved inorganic carbon from seawater is sequestered in carbonated sediments, and the average lifetime of these sediments. The average lifetime of sea floor today is about 60 million years, and it takes about 10 million years to circulate the entire ocean through hydrothermal vent systems. If the Earth was geologically more active during the Hadean, it is logical to conclude that both of these processes would have occurred at a faster rate then than they do now. If we assume that the *ratio* of these two numbers (sea-floor lifetime and the time required for seawater circulation through hydrothermal vents) has not changed over time and so was about 6 : 1, and also that dissolved inorganic carbon in hydrothermal vents was removed from seawater with 100% efficiency through carbonation reactions during the Hadean, then a given atom of carbon cycling between the ocean/atmosphere system and the sea floor would spend about six times longer on the sea floor (process B in Figure 10.1) than in the ocean/atmosphere (processes A and E in Figure 10.1). So, 85% (i.e. 5/6) of the carbon in the Hadean Earth would have been stored in the sea floor at any time, and 15% (i.e. 1/6) would have been stored in the ocean/atmosphere.

- If you assume a global total of 1×10^{20} kg of carbon, how much would there have been in the ocean/atmosphere and in sea-floor sediments, respectively, during the Hadean?

- 15% of the total would have been present in the ocean/atmosphere, i.e. $0.15 \times 1 \times 10^{20}$ kg, or 1.5×10^{19} kg of carbon, and therefore 8.5×10^{19} kg of carbon would have been present in the sea-floor sediments.

The important point here is not the exact ratio, but the fact that, according to this model, the combination of a high level of dissolved inorganic carbon in the seawater and the high tectonic activity means that a large proportion of the carbon in the early Earth could have been stored in primitive sea-floor sediments by carbonation reactions.

- If you assume that our estimate of 1.5×10^{19} kg of carbon in the Hadean ocean/atmosphere is of the right order of magnitude, how does this compare with the amount of carbon in the ocean/atmosphere of the modern Earth? (See Table 9.2.)

- There was about four hundred times more carbon in the atmosphere/ocean system during the Hadean than there is today.

Further partitioning this ocean/atmosphere carbon between the atmosphere and the ocean requires guesses about the chemistry of the Hadean ocean, particularly the ocean acidity, which would affect how much CO_2 is dissolved in the seawater. Unfortunately, the chemical composition of the Hadean ocean is highly uncertain – depending on the assumptions made, it could have been alkaline, acidic or neutral. If we assume the ocean was warmer and more acidic than today (due to the emission of acid sulfates and chlorides from volcanoes), proportionally less CO_2 would dissolve in the seawater and more would be in the atmosphere. A reasonable estimate puts about 1×10^{19} kg of carbon in the atmosphere and the remaining

0.5×10^{19} kg of carbon in the oceans. (You should recognize that there are many uncertainties in these numbers and they should be taken only as indications of the order of magnitude of the partitioning.)

The total mass of the Earth's atmosphere today is about 5.3×10^{18} kg (Table 9.1). Thus, if our maximum estimate for the Hadean is right, the mass of carbon in the atmosphere then was about double the *total* mass of the atmosphere today. And since there are about 7.6×10^{14} kg of carbon in the modern atmosphere as CO_2 (Table 9.2), the mass of carbon in the Hadean atmosphere would have been about 13 000 times higher than today's $[(1 \times 10^{19}$ kg$)/(7.6 \times 10^{14}$ kg$)]$! The Hadean oceans would have contained roughly an order of magnitude less carbon than the Hadean atmosphere, but this would still be some 100 times higher than the dissolved inorganic carbon concentration in today's oceans.

If we were to assume the atmosphere consisted entirely of CO_2 (a reasonable simplification for the Hadean), let us see what the atmospheric pressure due to CO_2 might have been if there were 1×10^{19} kg of carbon in the Hadean atmosphere. Following the method outlined in Box 1.2, we first convert this value of the mass of carbon into the mass of CO_2 by multiplying by 44/12 (the relative molecular mass of CO_2 is 44). We obtain a value of 3.67×10^{19} kg. To find the column mass, we divide this mass by the Earth's surface area, 5.1×10^{14} m^2:

$$(3.67 \times 10^{19} \text{ kg})/(5.1 \times 10^{14} \text{ m}^2) = 7.20 \times 10^4 \text{ kg m}^{-2}$$

To find the pressure, we multiply the column mass by g, the acceleration due to gravity, 9.8 m s^{-2}:

$$\text{pressure} = 7.20 \times 10^4 \text{ kg m}^{-2} \times 9.8 \text{ m s}^{-2} = 7.05 \times 10^5 \text{ N m}^{-2} = 7.05 \text{ Pa}$$

Now, 1 bar $= 1.013 \times 10^5$ Pa, or 1.013×10^5 N m^{-2}, so the pressure due to CO_2 is $(7.05 \times 10^5$ N m$^{-2})/(1.013 \times 10^5$ N m$^{-2})$, or about 7 bar. (For a discussion of the units used when discussing early atmospheres, see Box 10.1.)

Box 10.1 More on quantifying gases

Atmospheric gases today are commonly expressed in proportional terms, such as volume mixing ratios or mass mixing ratios, e.g. as a *percentage* or a number of *parts per million* of the total (by volume or by mass) of gas (Box 1.2). For instance, the Earth's atmosphere today contains about 360 p.p.m. (by volume) of carbon dioxide and 21% by volume of oxygen. This approach is fine for discussing today's atmosphere, or the Earth's atmosphere in the relatively-recent geological past, where we can assume that the total number of moles of gas in the atmosphere is not substantially different from that of today's. But what about much earlier in time, when it was likely that the atmosphere contained substantially more gas molecules (primarily carbon dioxide) than it does today? If the *total amount* of a substance changes, we can no longer compare proportional values.

For example, consider a hypothetical planet which today contains 10% of gas Z and 90% of gas X. Let us say the planet's atmosphere at some time in the past contained 5% of gas Z and 95% of gas X. At first glance, you might conclude that the atmosphere of the past contained less gas Z overall. But, in fact, all we know is that it contained *proportionally* less gas Z. To determine whether the *total* amount of gas Z was lower or higher, we need one more piece of information: the ratio between the total mass of the atmosphere of the planet in the past and that today. If the total mass of the atmosphere in the past was double that of today, there would be no change in the absolute amount of gas Z over time, even though its proportion of the total is less. For this reason we cannot compare over time atmospheric gases expressed in proportional units unless we are reasonably sure that the total amount of all gases in the atmosphere has remained substantially the same. We can, however, compare values based on the total *atmospheric pressure* that a gas exerts – this is directly related to the total amount of that gas in the atmosphere. For this reason, comparisons between atmospheric carbon dioxide levels in the geological past and the present are made on the basis of units of pressure (pascals or bars). Note that this is not such an important distinction for gases that were present in only trace quantities, such as atmospheric oxygen levels over the Cryptozoic.

10.4 The minimum atmospheric CO_2 level: the planetary energy balance equation

Let us turn now to the other end of the spectrum, and attempt to define a lower limit for atmospheric CO_2 in the Hadean. Setting a lower limit returns us to our assumption that the early Earth was warm and wet (Propositions 1 and 4). Specifically, we have no evidence that the oceans were *ever* frozen. We assume then, that the minimum amount of CO_2 on the early Earth was just sufficient to provide enough of a greenhouse effect to retain liquid oceans, i.e. to maintain a global mean surface temperature higher than around 0 °C.

The surface temperature of the Earth is an expression of the balance between the short-wave solar radiation arriving at the Earth's surface, and the long-wave radiation leaving it. If these quantities were not identical, the mean surface temperature of the Earth would either increase or decrease. If we know the amount of solar radiation arriving at any time, we can estimate the surface temperature the Earth would have in the absence of an atmosphere, in other words, the Earth's **effective temperature** (T_e). We start with an expression you have met elsewhere in the Course, the Stefan–Boltzmann Law for a perfect radiating black body:

$$\text{energy radiated per unit area per unit time} = \sigma T^4 \qquad \text{(Equation 10.1)}$$

where σ is a constant called the Stefan–Boltzmann constant and T is the temperature of the black body. (Temperature here is in kelvin rather than degrees Celsius.) Now, the radiant flux of long-wavelength energy *from* the Earth at any effective temperature must be equal to energy incident *on* it per unit area per unit time. This incident radiant flux is merely the amount of radiation received from the Sun. The amount of sunlight received at any time by the Earth is equal to a disc with surface area πr^2, but the Earth is actually a rotating sphere with surface area $4\pi r^2$. For this reason, if S is the solar radiant flux arriving at a distance of 150 million kilometres from the Sun, then the average amount received over the whole Earth's surface is $S/4$. At the present day, the radiation *from* the Sun is about 1370 W m^{-2}, so the average incident on the Earth is about 343 W m^{-2}.

Furthermore, the amount of radiation reaching the *surface* depends on the amount reflected by clouds, polar ice, etc. This fraction is the albedo. If we denote the albedo as A, then the fraction of energy not reflected (i.e. used in warming) is $1 - A$. Thus, we can write an expression for the effective temperature of the Earth as:

$$\sigma T_e^4 = \frac{S}{4}(1 - A) \qquad \text{(Equation 10.2)}$$

This is called the **planetary energy balance equation**.

■ According to Equation 10.2, would the effective temperature of a planet with albedo 0.5 be higher or lower than a planet with albedo 0.3?

■ The effective temperature would be lower, since $(1 - 0.5)$ is smaller than $(1 - 0.3)$. In other words a planet with a lighter surface reflects more sunlight and has a lower effective temperature than a planet with a darker surface.

▓   Use the planetary energy balance equation (Equation 10.2) to calculate the Earth's effective temperature at the present day. (Stefan–Boltzmann's constant $= 5.667 \times 10^{-8}$ W m^{-2} K^{-4} and $A = 0.3$.)

▓   If we substitute the given values into Equation 10.2, we find:

$$5.667 \times 10^{-8}\ \text{W m}^{-2}\text{K}^{-4} \times T_e^4 = 343\ \text{W m}^{-2} \times (1 - 0.3)$$

so

$$T_e^4 = \frac{240}{5.667 \times 10^{-8}\ \text{K}^{-4}} = 4.24 \times 10^9\ \text{K}^4$$
$$T_e = 255\ \text{K}$$

This is the surface temperature the Earth would have if it didn't have an atmosphere. (255 K = −18 °C)

Some of the radiation which is reflected from the Earth's surface and which the planetary energy balance equation considers lost to space is, however, not lost at all: it is absorbed and re-radiated by gases *in the atmosphere*, principally water vapour and carbon dioxide. This is the **greenhouse effect**. The difference between T_e, the effective temperature, and the current global mean surface temperature (GMST), T_s, of 288 K (15 °C), is maintained by the combined greenhouse effect of carbon dioxide, water and a few other gases. Thus, at the present day $T_s - T_e$ is equivalent to about 33 K (33 °C).

From observations of other stars and from long-standing theories of stellar evolution, astronomers have concluded that the Sun has gradually increased in luminosity over the last 4.6 billion years of its existence. As we saw elsewhere in the Course, the main reason for this is that as a star undergoes hydrogen fusion, its core contains proportionally more and more of the heavier elements, primarily helium, and gradually becomes more dense. If the core is more dense, it is hotter and hence has a greater luminosity. It has been estimated that 4.5 billion years ago, our Sun was probably some 25–30% less luminous than it is today.

You can use the planetary energy balance equation again to find the Earth's effective temperature 4.5 billion years ago when the Sun was about 30% less luminous by repeating the calculation with the new value for radiant flux (if you assume the albedo was not significantly different from today's). Verify that this gives an effective temperature of about 234 K, or −39 °C.

▓   If the greenhouse effect present today (about 33 K) due to water vapour and CO_2 were acting 4.5 billion years ago, would it have been sufficient to prevent freezing?

▓   No. The GMST, T_s, would have been 234 K + 33 K = 267 K (i.e. −6 °C).

Our calculations show, therefore, that when both the Earth and the Sun were young, the Earth's surface temperature should have been below freezing, *if the composition of the atmosphere had been the same as it is today*. But there is no evidence that the young Earth was a global icehouse.

This is the so-called **faint young Sun paradox**, first enunciated by Carl Sagan and George Mullen in 1972. It suggests that if the early Earth was similar to today's, and only warmed by direct solar radiation on its surface, it should have been a frozen ball of ice.

Of course, the faint young Sun paradox is only a 'paradox' if we don't consider an *enhanced* greenhouse effect. In fact, rather than being a paradox, the faint young Sun calculation suggests that abundant greenhouse gases *must* have been present on the early Earth – if only because life patently exists, and the Earth could not have been a perpetual icehouse.

Let us assume that the Earth's effective temperature (T_e) 4.5 billion years ago was about 234 K (–39 °C). The fact that the Earth was not frozen over means that the actual surface temperature (T_s) must have been *at least* 0 °C, and probably higher. The difference between the actual surface temperature and the effective temperature ($T_s - T_e$) would therefore have been 39 K (39 °C) (as opposed to today's 33 K). This could then be taken as the magnitude of the greenhouse effect in the early Earth. Now 'all' we have to do is to translate this greenhouse warming of 39 °C into the level of atmospheric CO_2.

This is easier said than done. We have to turn to models of how the Earth's climate is controlled; the so-called **general circulation models** (GCMs). These models are often used today for the opposite purpose: to estimate how much the Earth will warm if atmospheric CO_2 increases due to fossil fuel burning. They are simple in theory but complex in their calculations – they calculate an energy balance for the Earth. However, instead of balancing inputs and outputs for the whole Earth in a single calculation, GCMs divide the Earth into ever smaller grids and calculate the energy balances – including lateral transfers of energy – for each grid. Huge amounts of computing power are needed for all these calculations.

Like the planetary energy balance equation, the calculations assume a certain intensity of solar radiation, proportion of greenhouse gases in the atmosphere and planetary albedo. There is an additional complication in that water vapour is the most important greenhouse gas and there is a positive feedback loop between temperature and atmospheric water vapour content – the higher the temperature, the more water vapour the atmosphere can hold, and the greater the greenhouse effect. Conversely, at low temperatures there is less water and less of a greenhouse effect. Thus, the effect of water vapour is to greatly *amplify* the effect of other greenhouse gases such as carbon dioxide.

This argument should convince you that it is quite difficult to model the greenhouse effect, particularly for conditions that were significantly different from those that prevail today. However, it has been estimated that with a solar luminosity 30% lower than today's, an albedo of 0.3 and an atmosphere containing only water vapour and CO_2 as the greenhouse gases, the minimum amount of atmospheric CO_2 required to keep the Earth's temperature just above freezing in the Hadean was about 0.1 bar. This is about 280 times the present atmospheric level (PAL) of CO_2 of 0.000 36 bar. (For a review of how atmospheric pressure is used to express the quantity of a gas, see Boxes 1.2 and 10.1.)

To sum up our calculations so far, we have estimated that the level of atmospheric CO_2 for the Hadean Earth (between about 4.6 and 3.8 billion years ago) was somewhere between 7 and 0.1 bar (13 000 and 280 PAL). This is an enormous range, but even at the upper limit, a pressure of CO_2 of about 7 bar would still be considerably less than that on Venus today (about 93 bar). The Earth's temperature at even this upper level of atmospheric CO_2 would have been less than 100 °C – and life would have been possible.

What can we say, then, about how atmospheric CO_2 levels changed after the Hadean?

10.5 The change in the level of CO$_2$ over time

10.5.1 Changes in effective temperature

Even if there are large errors in our estimate that the minimum level of atmospheric CO$_2$ in the early atmosphere was 280 times that of today, it is still obvious that there has been a major decrease in the level of atmospheric CO$_2$ over time. The planetary energy balance equation described in the last section would also predict this decrease, for as the Sun continues to increase in luminosity, the amount of greenhouse warming (and thus CO$_2$) necessary to keep the planet from freezing over decreases. In theory, we could use this method to estimate the level of atmospheric CO$_2$ over the whole of the Earth's existence.

▪   What specific information would be required to calculate the effective temperature at any time in the Earth's history?

▪   We would have to know exactly how solar radiation has increased over time.

Astronomical work suggests that we can estimate the Sun's luminosity (directly related to radiation) at any point in time since the origin of the Solar System using the following expression:

$$S_t = \frac{S_o}{1 + \left[\dfrac{2}{5}\left(1 - \dfrac{t}{t_o}\right)\right]}$$ (Equation 10.3)

where S_o is the present solar luminosity (set arbitrarily as 1); S_t is the luminosity at any time t since the origin of the Solar System and t_o is the present age of the Sun (4.6 billion years).

▪   What should the solar luminosity have been 2.1 billion years after the birth of the Solar System?

▪   If we substitute the given values into Equation 10.3 we find:

$$S_{2.1} = \frac{1}{1 + \left[\dfrac{2}{5}\left(1 - \dfrac{2.1}{4.6}\right)\right]} = 0.82$$

Thus, the luminosity of the Sun when it was 2.1 billion years old was 82% of today's value. Alternatively, we could say that the Sun was 18% less luminous than today.

Figure 10.2 shows a plot of the calculated increase in solar luminosity since the origin of the Solar System 4.6 billion years ago (relative to the present luminosity, which is set at 1). It is nearly, but not quite, linear. Mark the point you have just calculated, which defines the Sun's luminosity at the beginning of the Proterozoic, one of the major milestones in the Earth's history. Remember you are marking 2.1 billion years *after* the origin of the (4.6-billion-year-old) Solar System, i.e. 4.6 – 2.1 = 2.5 billion years before the present.

Since we can estimate solar luminosity (and therefore radiation) at any particular time from Equation 10.3, we can put this value into Equation 10.2 to calculate the Earth's effective temperature at any time. Figure 10.3 shows such a plot of estimated effective temperature for the Earth over geological time. Comparing the two plots in Figure 10.3, it is obvious that as solar luminosity increases, so does the Earth's effective temperature.

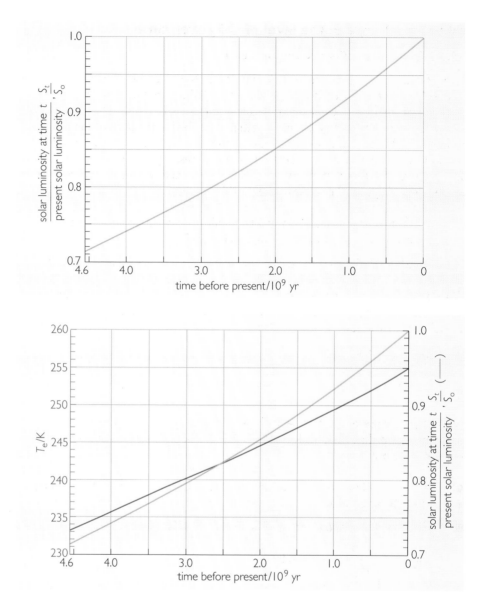

Figure 10.2
Variation in the relative solar luminosity (S_t/S_o) over geological time, where S_o is the present-day solar luminosity (set at 1) and S_t is the solar luminosity at time t.

Figure 10.3
Variation in the effective surface temperature (T_e) of the Earth over geological time, compared with the variation in relative solar luminosity S_t/S_o (from Figure 10.2).

Now that we have found a way of estimating T_e over time, we can use general circulation models to estimate the level of atmospheric CO_2 necessary to keep the surface of the Earth just above the freezing temperature of water as described in Section 10.4. This would give us a minimum estimate of atmospheric CO_2 over time. But perhaps, if we were to gather more evidence, we could set better limits on the Earth's surface temperature in the mid- and late Cryptozoic, thereby narrowing our range of estimated atmospheric CO_2. For now, let us concentrate on the available evidence about global mean surface temperature.

10.5.2 The Archean climate

Even after the main accretion phase had ended, the lunar record suggests that the Earth continued to be sporadically bombarded by large (100-km diameter) bodies until around 3.8 billion years ago. Following this period, the Earth was able to form a continental crust of lower-density granitic rocks from the mantle. Thus, the beginning of the Archean (about 3.8 billion years ago) was marked by the formation of continental rocks, which unlike the ocean floor cannot be destroyed by subduction. The 3.8-billion-year-old rocks from Isua, Western Greenland (Figure 10.4) contain both ancient sediments that were originally limestone (carbonate rock), sandstones formed by the action of water and 'pillow lavas' (lavas which cooled under water). These rocks therefore show unequivocally that there was a hydrosphere on Earth at that time and that dissolved inorganic carbon had already begun to react with dissolved calcium and magnesium ions in the seawater to form calcium and magnesium carbonates. As we have seen, the presence of liquid water sets a minimum estimate on the GMST of around 0 °C at 3.8 billion years ago.

The second major change that marks the Archean is the emergence of life. It is clear that 3.6 billion years ago microbial life was flourishing, as evidenced by fossilized stromatolites found in Australia. The earliest photosynthetic organisms were microscopic marine prokaryotes. Some microbes may have also started to colonize the early land surfaces, forming a thin film on rocks (although it is possible that high levels of ultraviolet radiation may have inhibited this). By the early Archean, then, atmospheric carbon (in the form of carbon dioxide) would have been fixed in organic matter in the sea (and possibly on land) and, as we have seen in previous chapters, a fraction of this organic carbon could have been converted into organic sediments for long-term storage.

But what of the climate at that time? At the present day, we know that life can be found existing under a vast range of conditions, but no ancient weather reports were left by the Earth's inhabitants during the Cryptozoic. To set boundaries on the climate, then, we must rely on our knowledge of chemistry and physics, and the few geological clues we can find.

We can set the maximum surface temperature that was likely to have occurred on the early Earth by looking for clues in the geological record. One clue is the presence throughout the rock record of sulfate minerals that were originally deposited in the form of **evaporitic gypsum**, $CaSO_4.2H_2O$ (Figure 10.5). This mineral is known to lose its associated water molecules and to be converted into the **anhydrite** (water-free) form ($CaSO_4$) at temperatures above 58 °C. Evaporitic gypsum deposits can be found from as far back as about 3.5 billion years ago, and are still forming at the present day. These give us a rough upper limit for the surface temperature – assuming the evaporitic gypsum has not been recrystallized from the original anhydrite since deposition. Based on this evidence, it is reasonable to suppose that since about 3.5 billion years ago, the mean surface temperature of the Earth has not been above 58 °C.

Figure 10.4
The 3.8-billion-year-old rocks from Isua, Western Greenland show evidence of (flattened) pillow lavas. The pillows are composed of fine-grained amphibolite (basalts which have been metamorphosed at about 400–500 °C) in one of the few areas of relatively low deformation. Mostly, in this region, the high degree of deformation more or less completely flattens the pillows.

Figure 10.5
Modern evaporite gypsum from Salar de San Martin, north Chile forms a white crust on this lake. These were formed in an internal basin ringed by volcanoes at high altitude (3500 m) in the central Andes.

10.5.3 The Proterozoic: heat waves and glaciers

By the beginning of the Proterozoic, continental land was forming rapidly. Geological evidence of conditions on Earth is correspondingly much more abundant. And the rocks contain evidence that the climate oscillated between quite wide extremes during this period.

There is evidence for two Ice Ages during the Proterozoic: the Huronian glaciation of about 2.3 billion years ago (named after the region in Canada where the glacial deposits were first discovered), and a Late Precambrian series of glaciations between about 850 and 615 million years ago. (We have used 'Precambrian' here rather than 'Cryptozoic' as this is the name usually given to this period of glaciation.) The clues that help geologists to identify glacial deposits include **striated rock surfaces** (Figure 10.6), where boulders transported in ice gouged grooves in the bedrock; and **tills**, a mixture of clay and boulders left where glaciers melt and drop the load they have carried. One can see similar deposits today in the **moraines** (glacial deposits) on the margins of active glaciers. By mapping and dating such deposits, the extent and duration of each glaciation can be determined. Evidence of extensive glaciation during these ancient Ice Ages is well established, but the details of their extent and timing are not.

Figure 10.6
Rock surface polished and striated by the passage of a glacier. This example is from the Bolivian Andes, and dates only to the last glacial maximum (at about 18 000 years ago), but similar traces of ancient glaciations can be found where they are exposed from beneath overlying deposits.

Note that evidence of glaciation is not evidence in itself of an Ice Age. Glaciation simply means that snowfall exceeds melting so that over a given time period ice and snow build up. Some glacial deposits could simply reflect *local* cold conditions. It is only when these deposits are found over extensive regions and their formation extends over a long duration can we justifiably consider that period of time an Ice Age. And finally, remember that glacial deposits found today at a certain location on the planet do not necessarily imply that glaciers ever existed at that particular latitude and longitude – continents drift, carrying evidence of glaciation with them. Glacial deposits found today in Australia or Africa, for instance, may well have been formed when those continents were over the South Pole! So in order to relate glaciations to *global* climate, we need to have a good idea of the latitudes of the continents at the time when glacial deposits were laid down. There are paleomagnetic techniques for doing this – but we will not go into these here.

Dates for the Huronian glaciation cluster around 2.3 billion years ago. Most of the rocks containing this evidence occur in North America, South Africa and Australia, but the glaciation may have been more extensive, as mid-Cryptozoic rocks are fairly rare. We also do not have a good idea of the latitudes of the continents at the time. The Late Precambrian glaciation appears to have been a series of global glaciations separated by warmer periods, extending from about 850 to 615 million years ago. Glacial deposits from this period are found in all continents except Antarctica (where they may well exist but have not yet been found). Some deposits found in Australia indicate that the Late Precambrian glaciation may even have affected what were then tropical regions, suggesting that it may have been exceptionally severe.

What can these two Proterozoic Ice Ages tell us about global surface temperature at that time? We know from geological and fossil evidence that there was no polar ice during the Mesozoic (between 245 and 65 million years ago), when global mean surface temperature (GMST) was thought to be about 25 °C, i.e. 10 °C warmer than today's GMST. We also know that today's polar ice-caps appeared 20 million years ago, when the mean surface temperature was about 20 °C. Therefore, it seems reasonable to set 20 °C as an *upper* limit on the GMST during global glacial periods. In fact, it is likely that the GMST was considerably colder than 20 °C, especially for the severe Late Precambrian glaciation. Given the inferred presence of glaciers in the tropics, it is probable that the Earth was colder than at any time in its subsequent history, with a GMST probably closer to 10 °C than 20 °C. So, we shall halve this value and arbitrarily set 5 °C as a reasonable *lower* limit for this period.

A note of caution is called for here. Although much of the Northern Hemisphere was covered by more than a kilometre of ice only 20 000 years ago, evidence of this great glaciation can be elusive. It was only in the 19th century that geologists agreed that it had actually taken place. Much of the most convincing evidence lies in rather superficial features like ice-sculpted land forms and 'erratic' (ice-deposited) boulders. Moraines are rarely more than a few tens of metres thick, and can easily be confused with other deposits. Even if these moraines survived to be preserved in the geological record, it would be difficult to identify them with certainty as being of glacial origin. Thus, while the evidence of ancient glaciations is widely accepted, it is not *universally* accepted. There have even been suggestions that some ancient deposits which have been interpreted as being of glacial origin may be from an entirely different source, such as ejecta from large impact events or deposits formed on the sea floor that have nothing to do with glaciers.

■   Would the absence of glacial deposits from certain ages in the geological record necessarily imply there were no glaciers at that time?

■   No. It is possible that some glacial deposits have not yet been discovered, have been destroyed over time, or have not been recognized as such by geologists.

To sum up, geological evidence suggests that the GMST of the Earth has probably not exceeded 58 °C, nor fallen below 0 °C for at least the last 3.5 billion years. These limits may be further constrained by two glacial periods in the Cryptozoic, one at around 2.3 billion years ago and one from about 850 to 615 billion years ago. A reasonable range for GMST over these periods can be set at between 5 and 20 °C.

10.5.4 Energy Balance model for atmospheric CO_2

Narrowing the range of plausible surface temperatures for the Cryptozoic Ice Ages gives us a slightly better idea of the climate during those periods in Earth history. Jim Kasting, an American atmospheric scientist, developed a model to estimate the level of atmospheric CO_2 during those Ice Ages, using the planetary energy balance equation described in Section 10.4. He assumed that the Earth's albedo remained constant over time, and that solar luminosity increased as shown in Figure 10.2. Kasting used the range of global mean surface temperatures estimated from by the glacial deposits (5–20 °C) as 'target' temperatures for his model.

The model – which we shall call the **Energy Balance model** – also assumes that the only other important greenhouse gas besides CO_2 and water vapour is ozone. It may surprise you to see ozone as an important greenhouse gas, but in addition to absorbing solar radiation strongly in the short-wave ultraviolet wavelengths (Chapter 8), ozone also absorbs long-wave infrared radiation. Depending on its concentration, ozone could increase mean surface temperature by up to 5 °C, thereby reducing the amount of CO_2 required to achieve the target surface temperature. Ozone concentration is related to the level of molecular oxygen at any time, so the model also requires estimates for atmospheric oxygen over the times of the two glacial periods.

▓　　From your answer to Activity 3.1, what would you roughly estimate the atmospheric oxygen level to have been about 2.3 billion years ago and about 0.8 billion years ago with respect to present atmospheric levels?

▓　　About 0.01 PAL 2.3 billion years ago and about 0.05 – 0.1 PAL 0.8 billion years ago.

The Energy Balance model assumes atmospheric oxygen levels 2.3 billion years ago to have been between 0 and 0.03 PAL, and 0.8 billion years ago to have been between 0.03 and 1 PAL. The model then enables surface temperature to be calculated as a function of atmospheric CO_2 levels for the two glacial periods (Figure 10.7). The width of the shaded bands gives the variation in the estimate due to the range in estimates for atmospheric oxygen at each time period. We have postulated that the average surface temperature during these glacial periods was somewhere between 5 and 20 °C. Now try Activity 10.1 to pull this information together to estimate atmospheric CO_2 levels over the two glacial periods in the Cryptozoic.

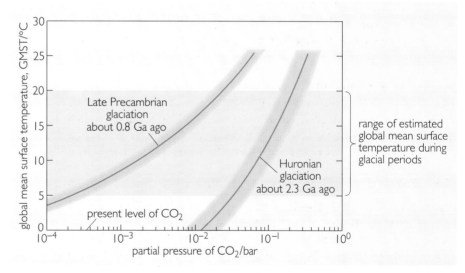

Figure 10.7
Surface temperature as a function of the atmospheric CO_2 levels calculated using Kasting's Energy Balance model for two glacial periods at about 0.8 and 2.3 billion years ago. The green shaded bands represent the variation in calculated surface temperature based on the assumed range in the level of atmospheric oxygen (the mean values are represented by the lines).

Note that 'mean minimum level of CO_2' and 'mean maximum level of CO_2' in Table 10.1 do not represent the true range of error in the estimates, they represent the mean values at either end of the range of estimated temperatures (i.e. at 5 and 20 °C). To find the true range of error in these estimates we would have to take into account all the assumptions of the model, and this is impractical for present purposes. Nonetheless, Kasting's Energy Balance model can still give a 'best estimate' to show how atmospheric CO_2 levels have varied throughout geological time (Figure 10.8). You should verify that the four values you added to Table 10.1 fall within the range of atmospheric CO_2 given in Figure 10.8. (Remember that you calculated the upper estimate for atmospheric CO_2 over the Hadean using a different method (Section 10.3) and therefore have, in Table 10.1, a slightly different maximum CO_2 estimate from that shown in Figure 10.8.)

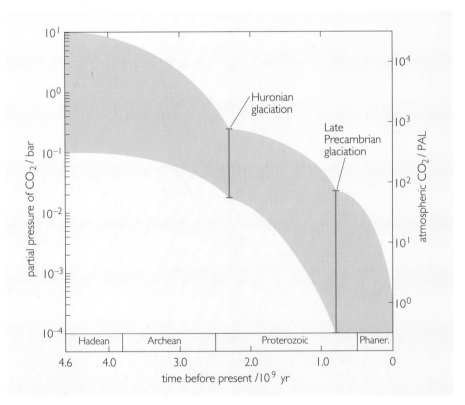

Figure 10.8 Variation in atmospheric CO_2 levels throughout geological time as calculated by the Kasting's Energy Balance model. The range of values during the two periods of glaciation are marked by the bars.

■   Why are the inferred CO_2 levels so much higher for the Huronian glaciation than for the Late Precambrian glaciation, although surface temperatures were estimated to be in the same range?

■   The Sun was fainter earlier in the Earth's history. Thus, to achieve the same surface temperature with a lower contribution from solar radiation, a higher concentration of greenhouse gases (e.g. CO_2) would be required during the earlier (Huronian) glaciation.

In summary, Kasting's Energy Balance model suggests that atmospheric CO_2 has declined over the Cryptozoic from levels ranging from 7 to 0.1 bar at the start of the Cryptozoic to levels ranging between 10^{-2} and 10^{-4} bar at the end of the Cryptozoic.

10.6 Examining the assumptions in the Energy Balance model

10.6.1 Introduction

The next important step in any modelling exercise is to examine critically the assumptions on which the model is based in the light of independent evidence. This is can be a difficult step – no one wants to deliberately shoot down their own beautiful model, theory, or experiment. However, testing the assumptions used is critically important in appreciating the limits of any model.

■   Before reading on, take a few moments to look back over the development of the Energy Balance model described in this chapter, and list some of the important assumptions that have been made.

■   These are some of the important ones:

♦   That global mean surface temperature, periods of global glaciation, and atmospheric CO_2 levels are linked in a predictable way.

♦   That the Earth's albedo has not changed over time.

♦   That water vapour, carbon dioxide and ozone are the only important greenhouse gases in the atmosphere.

We shall now evaluate these three assumptions in greater detail.

10.6.2 The carbon dioxide–global temperature link

We have assumed so far that atmospheric CO_2 levels and GMST are connected in some way. Certainly we have abundant evidence of a runaway CO_2-linked greenhouse effect on Venus, and unambiguous experimental data showing that CO_2 absorbs infrared radiation. However, the Energy Balance model relies on an explicit, quantifiable correlation between atmospheric CO_2 levels and GMST. We need to find independent evidence that this correlation is valid.

To find such evidence, we need a simultaneous record of both atmospheric CO_2 and temperature over a long period of time. We have a continuous record of CO_2 directly measured from the atmosphere for only the last few decades. But fortunately, using some scientific detective work, we can actually measure atmospheric CO_2 levels much further back in time, to about 220 000 years ago. These data come from the air trapped in the ice that has accumulated since the last glacial period in the polar regions of Greenland and Antarctica (Box 10.2).

Box 10.2 Air trapped in polar ice

Each year snow that falls on the polar ice-caps goes through a thaw and re-freeze cycle and becomes buried under successive layers of new snow and ice. Any given sample remains in contact with the outside air for a number of years, depending on how quickly the snow transforms to ice and on the rate of accumulation of the snow. Eventually, once the sample is buried between around 50 and 100 m below the surface, the sample is effectively sealed off from the outside. At this time a record of the outside air is preserved. (The air that is finally trapped and sealed in bubbles in the ice is a mixture of different ages, from roughly 10 to 300 years old.) By drilling a deep core through the ice, scientists can sample a sequential record of trapped air that may go back over more than 100 000 years.

At the time of writing, the oldest ice core is the 2546-metre Vostok core drilled in eastern Antarctica (Figure 10.9). It is difficult to go much deeper than the depth of the Vostok core, because the immense pressure at these depths eventually causes the lowest layers of ice to flow, so destroying the record from the earlier periods.

Measuring the CO_2 content of the trapped air

Figure 10.9
A sample from the Vostok ice core, eastern Antarctica.

bubbles is relatively straightforward. It is more difficult to determine the temperature at the time when the air was trapped, but it can be inferred from the isotopic composition of the water that forms the ice.

  Which of the elements in water has more than one isotope?

■ Both hydrogen *and* oxygen have multiple isotopes.

Oxygen has three stable isotopes ^{16}O, ^{17}O and ^{18}O. Over 99% of natural oxygen is made up of ^{16}O, with ^{18}O comprising most of the balance. The $^{18}O/^{16}O$ ratio in the ice relative to that in a seawater standard is expressed as $\delta^{18}O$, measured in parts per thousand, ‰. (This is analogous to the $\delta^{13}C$ values you met earlier in this book.) Hydrogen has two

stable isotopes, ^{1}H hydrogen and ^{2}H deuterium (or D), and a radioactive isotope ^{3}H tritium. The $D/^{1}H$ ratio relative to a seawater standard is expressed as δD.

Now, when seawater evaporates, the lighter isotopes evaporate more readily than the heavier isotopes, so water vapour is relatively enriched in ^{16}O and ^{1}H and depleted in ^{18}O and D. When the global mean surface temperature is lower, large quantities of water are lost from the ocean and stored as ice. The snow is more depleted in ^{18}O relative to ^{16}O, while the water that remains in the ocean is more enriched in ^{18}O (and also D). Therefore, a lower $\delta^{18}O$ and δD ratio in an ice core indicates a period of lower temperature.

So, the concentration of CO_2 is analysed directly from the air trapped in ice, and the

contemporary temperature can be estimated from the isotopic ratios of the oxygen and hydrogen in the ice. In principal, then we could plot the temperature variation over time and CO_2 variation over time, and examine the two plots for any correlation.

■ What is the problem with this method?

■ If the air takes up to a several hundred years to accumulate before being isolated from the atmosphere, the ice is older than the air it traps.

So, at each level in an ice core, the following parameters must be measured or estimated:

◆ the age of the trapped air;
◆ the age of the ice trapping the air;
◆ the concentration of CO_2 in the trapped air;
◆ the $\delta^{18}O$ and δD isotopic ratios of the ice.

Models of snowfall accumulation at the site of the core are used to estimate the date at which the snow was deposited, while the age of the air is estimated with models of the rate of air diffusion through snow and ice.

Figure 10.10 shows the record of variation in CO_2 levels together with the estimated temperature from the Vostok ice core over a full glacial–interglacial cycle. You can see that there is a strong correlation between the pattern of this fine-scale variation in levels of atmospheric CO_2 and temperature (here estimated by using the δD isotopic ratio). This correlation is particularly marked at the start of the deglaciation (warming) events at about 130 000 years and 15 000 years ago. Whether atmospheric CO_2 levels are a *response* to the temperature fluctuations or a *cause* of them is a matter of considerable debate.

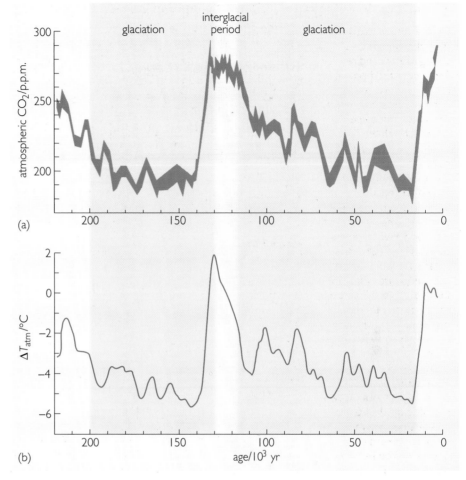

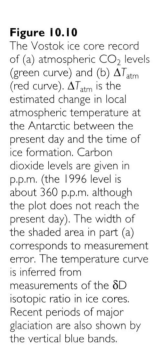

Figure 10.10
The Vostok ice core record of (a) atmospheric CO_2 levels (green curve) and (b) ΔT_{atm} (red curve). ΔT_{atm} is the estimated change in local atmospheric temperature at the Antarctic between the present day and the time of ice formation. Carbon dioxide levels are given in p.p.m. (the 1996 level is about 360 p.p.m. although the plot does not reach the present day). The width of the shaded area in part (a) corresponds to measurement error. The temperature curve is inferred from measurements of the δD isotopic ratio in ice cores. Recent periods of major glaciation are also shown by the vertical blue bands.

Note that the temperature deduced from the ice core is a *local* temperature. However, it is reasonable to assume that any fluctuation in global mean temperature would be reflected over the long term in local temperatures. For our purposes it is enough that the ice core record demonstrates that global mean temperature and atmospheric CO_2 have been closely linked, at least for the last 220 000 years.

10.6.3 The Earth's albedo

The Energy Balance model assumes a constant value for the Earth's albedo over time, i.e. that cloudiness and ice cover were the same in the past as they are now. These would affect the amount of solar radiation reaching the Earth's surface.

Formation of clouds is a poorly understood phenomenon. Among other factors, cloud formation is increased when there are more atmospheric aerosol particles for water to condense on. So if the concentration of atmospheric aerosols decreases, cloudiness may decrease as well. Today, one major source of cloud condensation nuclei is the gas **dimethyl sulfide** (DMS), which is produced by marine micro-organisms in the open ocean and released to the atmosphere. On oxidation of the sulfide in the atmosphere, stable sulfate aerosols form, and these provide cloud nuclei. In the early history of the Earth, the possible absence of these micro-organisms and the DMS they manufacture *may* have meant that global cloud cover was less than found today.

Or maybe not. Given that the composition of the atmosphere was quite different from today's, it is possible that there were other aerosols, e.g. from volcanic emissions, that acted as cloud condensation nuclei. And if the early Earth was warmer than today, increased evaporation may have *increased* cloudiness. You can see that we are rapidly going in circles!

To make matters worse, even if the amount of cloudiness over time were known, the effect of cloud cover on surface temperature is still uncertain. Increasing cloudiness can act as an important negative feedback on surface temperature by reflecting the Sun's radiation (think of the momentary relief when a cloud passes overhead on a hot summer day). Conversely, clouds can *warm* the Earth's surface by trapping heat that would otherwise escape from the surface (think how much warmer cloudy nights are than clear nights of sharp frost). Whether increasing cloudiness produces a net cooling or warming depends on the type and altitude of the cloud. Overall, satellite data indicate that the net effect of clouds on the global climate system is to cool the Earth's surface because of their overriding effect on the global albedo.

Changes in global ice and snow cover also affect the Earth's albedo. Although glacial deposits help us to reconstruct the extent and duration of Ice Age glaciations quite well, estimating global *amounts* of ice and snow over the Cryptozoic glacial and interglacial periods requires much guesswork. Since climate models for the Earth *today* cannot reproduce cloud, snow and ice feedbacks satisfactorily, it is a tall order to ask this of models for climate more than 2 billion years ago.

10.6.4 Other greenhouse gases

The Energy Balance CO_2 model considers water vapour, carbon dioxide and ozone to be the only greenhouse gases of importance. If high concentrations of methane were in the atmosphere at any time in the Earth's history, however, the amount of CO_2 necessary to achieve a given surface temperature for the model would be considerably less.

There is some evidence that this may have indeed been the case, for at least the early part of the Earth's history (as mentioned in Section 5.4). During the Archean, when atmospheric oxygen levels were low, early organisms may well have metabolized elements other than oxygen. In all likelihood there were methanogenic bacteria, organisms that metabolized CO_2 and hydrogen or simple organic compounds and in doing so released methane. The presence of these bacteria is supported by isotope evidence from late Archean kerogens (about 2.7 billion years old): in the Schidlowski diagram (Figure 3.8) there are pronounced negative dips in $\delta^{13}C_{org}$ values at about 2.7 billion years ago and again at 2.1 billion years ago. By modern standards, the carbon in these deposits is isotopically extremely light ($\delta^{13}C_{org}$ values of -35 to $-50‰$). It has been argued that these can be achieved by multiple fractionation of organic carbon in a primitive carbon cycle dominated by methane. This in turn requires high concentrations of methane in the sea and, by implication, the atmosphere.

Arguments from the carbon isotope record suggest that atmospheric methane could have been higher by at least a factor of 50 above present atmospheric levels when oxygen levels were low in the Archean. This in turn would require lower atmospheric CO_2 levels (some 15–20 times lower) to compensate for the estimated surface temperature. Over time, the role of methane as a potential additional greenhouse gas would probably have declined. Since methane is only stable in a reducing atmosphere, its atmospheric residence time is bound to have decreased in the Proterozoic as aerobic organisms began to dominate the seas and atmospheric oxygen levels rose accordingly.

10.7 Checking the independent evidence

Take another look at Figure 10.8. Now reflect on what the figure is based on. Using not much more that a few clues (evidence for liquid water on Earth, increasing solar luminosity and glacial deposits) we have reconstructed the evolution of atmospheric CO_2 levels over the entire history of the Earth. Granted, the errors are fairly large and difficult to quantify, and unfortunately there are no eyewitnesses from the time to corroborate the story of how the atmospheric CO_2 level has evolved. So how can the model be checked?

The answer is to look for any possible *independent* evidence of CO_2 levels from this period. That is, evidence that was *not* used in constructing the model.

In Section 4.2.4, we used evidence from fossil soils (paleosols) to draw some inferences about the nature of the atmosphere at the time when they were formed. A crucial factor was the mobility of iron: if the soil formed from a given parent rock is depleted in iron relative to the parent, then we can infer something about the ratio in the soil water of oxygen (tending to oxidize and precipitate the iron as a solid, Fe^{3+}) to carbonic acid (tending to remove it in solution as Fe^{2+} ions). By further inference, this provides a pointer to the ratio between oxygen and CO_2 in the atmosphere. When the Denison and Pronto paleosols were deposited about 2.4 billion years ago, this ratio was estimated to be between about 0.2 and 2, compared with about 600 today.

It is much more difficult to go from this estimate of the *ratio* of O_2 to CO_2 in the atmosphere to the *absolute* levels of oxygen and CO_2 in the atmosphere. Soil gas chemistry is complex, and requires knowledge of both the concentrations of the gases dissolved in rainwater, and the rate at which they diffuse from the atmosphere into soils. However, the best estimates from these paleosols of the partial pressure of CO_2 between 1.8 and 2.5 billion years ago are in the range 3×10^{-3} to 1.2×10^{-2} bar.

Another way of deducing ancient CO_2 levels is to restrict our study to soils that we can be reasonably sure formed in a very low oxygen environment, say, before 2.2 billion years ago. In this environment, iron is reduced and lost from the top of the soil profile. The iron may either be washed out of the profile into the groundwater or re-precipitated. Since there is not enough oxygen to precipitate the iron as iron *oxide*, it is precipitated as either iron *carbonate* ($FeCO_3$) if the soil CO_2 concentration is high, or an iron *silicate* mineral if the soil CO_2 is lower than that required to precipitate iron carbonate. Geochemists estimate that iron carbonate precipitation would have occurred at atmospheric CO_2 levels of approximately 100 times the present-day value and higher. At atmospheric CO_2 levels below this value, iron would have been precipitated as a silicate mineral.

None of the ancient paleosols so far found (aged between 2.2 and 2.7 billion years old) contain iron carbonate. This suggests that the partial pressure of CO_2 was lower than about 0.036 bar during this period within the Archean–Proterozoic.

▓ How do the estimates of CO_2 levels from iron mobility and iron carbonate compare with the CO_2 level for the same periods inferred from the Energy Balance model (Figure 10.8)?

▓ The estimated values from iron mobility (3×10^{-3} to 1.2×10^{-2} bar) is just within the range of calculated CO_2 levels for the mid-Proterozoic but is lower than the value predicted for the early Proterozoic. The estimate from iron carbonate data (0.036 bar) lies within the range of the lowest limit of the calculated CO_2 curve for 2.7 billion years ago – but only just.

Thus, the independent evidence from paleosols suggests the atmospheric CO_2 level was higher during the early Proterozoic than today, but not as high as the Energy Balance model suggests. Both ways of looking at the paleosol data suggest that the model may be somewhat overestimating levels of atmospheric CO_2. This is just the sort of result we would like to find from our independent evidence: a signal that we are on the right track, and an indication of the direction that further refinement should take. To refine the model, we could go back and evaluate the assumptions used, particularly those which allow CO_2 levels to be lower in the model. One likely candidate is that more methane could have existed in the atmosphere than the model assumes, augmenting the greenhouse effect and therefore requiring a lower level of CO_2. Another is that the Earth's albedo may have been less than today's, perhaps because of lower DMS emission from the sea providing fewer cloud condensation nuclei. As more evidence accumulates, it is likely that the estimated level of atmospheric CO_2 over the Cryptozoic as deduced from the Energy Balance model will be revised downwards. But at least we have made a start.

10.8 Ultimate causes for the decline in atmospheric CO_2

From the model, CO_2 declines over time because solar radiation increases, therefore less CO_2 is needed to maintain the 'target' global temperature. But this is simply equation balancing and says nothing about the ultimate *reason* for CO_2 decline. So why does atmospheric CO_2 decrease and where does it go?

We have deliberately avoided in-depth discussion of controls on atmospheric CO_2; this will be the topic of Chapter 11. However, we can say with confidence that most of the Earth's atmospheric CO_2 was steadily transferred to the sea-floor sediments (and crust) over the Cryptozoic, and that this was due to the effects of increasing solar radiation, the emergence of land and the evolution of life. Atmospheric CO_2 dissolves in rain and seawater to form carbonic acid, which then weathers rocks and soil and forms bicarbonate ions. All other things being equal, the rate of weathering would have been enhanced by any increases in global surface temperature which might have occurred due to steadily increasing solar luminosity. The net effect of weathering is to remove CO_2 from the atmosphere to the sea as dissolved inorganic carbon. Along continental shelf areas, some of this dissolved carbon can be precipitated with calcium, magnesium or iron to form carbonate deposits and eventually carbonate rock. Carbonate rock forms an enormous sink for most of the Earth's inorganic carbon. Significant amounts of carbon would also have been sequestered by organisms as organic carbon, some of which can also be buried and stored in sedimentary deposits. In this way, a progressive transfer of carbon from the atmosphere to the oceans and finally to sediments and rocks has taken place over geological time.

The two major glacial periods which occur near the beginning and the end of the Proterozoic allowed us to make a more precise estimate of the level of atmospheric CO_2 because they narrowed the range of global mean surface temperature that is used in the Energy Balance model. It is still not clear what caused these glaciations, however. The first (at about 2.3 billion years ago) was probably caused by a major episode of mountain building which rapidly removed CO_2 from the atmosphere as the newly-exposed sediments were weathered. The second was probably related to enhanced weathering as well. This period appears to be one of great tectonic activity which, besides exposing more land to weathering, may have also made conditions favourable for increased phytoplankton productivity in the sea by releasing nutrients from land. Soil microbes may have also become established by the late Proterozoic. These could have removed CO_2 through photosynthesis and also enhanced weathering (as we shall see in Chapter 11). All of these developments would have contributed to removal of atmospheric CO_2, and may have triggered the series of Ice Ages observed in the geological record.

The position of the continents may have also contributed to causing the Late Precambrian glaciation. If the land surface of the Earth was mostly distributed along the equatorial belt, as some evidence indicates, then higher solar radiation and, hence, higher surface temperature of the continents could have increased the rate of silicate weathering. Enhanced CO_2 removal due to this weathering could, paradoxically, have caused global cooling, possibly enough to trigger an Ice Age. Unfortunately, because these Ice Ages occurred so far back in geological time, with so little hard evidence of conditions on the Earth, their ultimate causes continue to be a matter of speculation.

10.9 Summary of Chapter 10

1 The Earth's earliest secondary atmosphere probably contained high concentrations of CO_2 outgassed from its hot interior. Before the emergence of significant land masses, carbon would have been partitioned between the atmosphere, the oceans and the sediments. One estimate puts about 85% of this inorganic carbon in the early sea-floor sediments, giving an upper limit to the level of atmospheric CO_2 of over 13 000 PAL, or a pressure of some 7 bar. These estimates are subject to large errors, but it is reasonably certain that the level of atmospheric CO_2 was relatively high in the early history of the Earth and that it has decreased steadily over time.

2 Because there are few data extending as far back as the Hadean, we use the Energy Balance model to calculate the level of atmospheric CO_2 which would allow the surface temperature of the Earth to remain within the range which is consistent with geological evidence. This evidence indicates that the Earth's temperature has remained between 0 and 58 °C for the last 3.5 billion years.

3 Results from the Energy Balance model suggest that the level of atmospheric CO_2 has declined steeply from between about 7 to 0.1 bar (about 13 000 to 280 PAL) in the early Hadean to between 10^{-2} and 10^{-4} bar (about 30–1 PAL) near the end of the Proterozoic. The main reason for the decline in the level of atmospheric CO_2 predicted by the Energy Balance model is the steadily increasing solar radiation. This need not, however, be the sole *cause* of the decline, since the model is an empirical one. Emergence of land and the evolution of life both accelerated removal of atmospheric CO_2.

4 Paleosol data are broadly consistent with the lowest modelled estimates of atmospheric CO_2 from the Energy Balance model.

5 A likely overestimate of atmospheric CO_2 levels by the Energy Balance model could be accounted for if high concentrations of methane augmented the greenhouse effect of CO_2 during the Cryptozoic. Also cloudiness, and therefore albedo, may have varied in ways unaccounted for by the model. It is likely that refining these values used in the Energy Balance model will lead to a lower estimate of the level of atmospheric CO_2 levels over the Cryptozoic.

6 The decline in atmospheric CO_2 levels over geological time is caused by the transfer of a significant amount of carbon from the atmosphere to the oceans, and finally to the sediments and rocks.

Now try the following questions to consolidate your understanding of this chapter.

Question 10.1

How do the processes that are thought to have controlled the levels of atmospheric CO_2 during the Hadean compare with those operating today? What are the major carbon sinks today? How do they differ from the major sinks we have postulated for the Hadean?

Question 10.2

How would the results of the Energy Balance model appear if solar luminosity remained constant at a level 30% lower than today's over the whole of the Cryptozoic? What evidence would you use to argue that this situation did not arise?

Question 10.3

You discover three paleosols aged at 2.8 ($\pm$0.2) billion years and estimate the level of atmospheric CO_2 at the time of their formation to be between 4.3×10^{-3} and 0.01 bar. How does this evidence compare with the level of CO_2 estimated from the Energy Balance model; Figure 10.8? Can you suggest some new assumptions that may be considered in the model in the light of the 'new evidence'?

Chapter 11
A process-based model of atmospheric carbon dioxide levels during the Phanerozoic

11.1 Introduction

Notwithstanding its limitations, the Energy Balance model described in Chapter 10 indicated that the level of atmospheric CO_2 has probably decreased considerably over time, although no reason was given as to *how* or *why* it may have decreased. In this chapter, the model we explore takes a different approach. It assumes that the processes controlling the level of atmospheric CO_2 are not just interesting, they are *integral* to the model. So before going into the details of the model itself, we will briefly review these processes. We shall start with a general discussion of stabilizing controls on the carbon cycle, then focus attention on the specific sources and sinks of atmospheric CO_2.

In Box 11.1, the concept of how the size of a reservoir may be changed as a result of altering the balance between sources and sinks is illustrated through an analogy. Although you have already come across feedback mechanisms, it is such an important concept that it is worth having a closer a look at it. At any given time, the level of atmospheric CO_2 is controlled by the dynamic balance between the rate of CO_2 entering the atmosphere from carbon *sources* and the rate of CO_2 removal from the atmosphere through carbon *sinks* (Figure 11.1a). As long as the sources balance the sinks, the amount of carbon dioxide in the atmosphere neither increases nor decreases. But what if the controls are temporarily out of balance, for instance, if the sources exceed the sinks (Figure 11.1b)? Then the level of atmospheric CO_2 would increase.

Now, if the rate of CO_2 removal into carbon sinks always remained the same, despite the increased supply from the sources, atmospheric CO_2 levels would continue to increase until the reservoir supplying the source was depleted. However, if the rate of carbon removal into the sinks were to increase as atmospheric CO_2 levels increased, then eventually the sink would again equal the source and a new dynamic balance would be achieved, but one with a higher level of atmospheric CO_2 (Figure 11.1c).

■   How would you describe a process by which an increase in the level of atmospheric CO_2 triggers an increase in the rate of removal of CO_2?

■   It is a negative feedback.

The magnitude of the feedback effect varies with the size of the CO_2 reservoir. A larger reservoir of atmospheric CO_2 promotes a larger negative feedback and therefore a higher rate of CO_2 removal. As the reservoir size decreases, the feedback effect decreases as well.

Box 11.1 Negative feedback on sinks: an analogy

Consider a house containing four cats, an entrance catflap and an exit catflap. Consider also that the rate of exit of cats is related to the frequency at which any cat inside the house passes by the exit catflap. If, over any given time period, the number of cats entering the house exactly equals the number exiting the house, there will be no net increase in the number of cats in the house. This is the situation in Figure 11.1a (*opposite*).

Now, suppose that this situation changes, and suddenly there are three cats entering the house for every one leaving it (Figure 11.1b). Therefore, over any given time period, the number of cats in the house increases by 2. This situation would continue indefinitely if the rate of exit of cats was unrelated to the total number of cats in the house. But we know it is not: the more cats in the house, the greater the chance that any one cat will leave through the catflap. Therefore, the rate at which cats leaves the house begins to increase (Figure 11.1c). In general terms – *the rate of removal or addition to a reservoir may not be constant but is often proportional to the reservoir size.* At the point when the number of cats leaving the house exactly matches the number entering, the number of cats in the house no longer increases (Figure 11.1d). The new reservoir size is stabilized – but at a *higher* level. This is a type of negative feedback.

This provides us with a proposition:

If, for a given time period, we can estimate the magnitude of the negative feedback between the atmospheric CO_2 reservoir size and the CO_2 removal rate, and can calculate the rates of the major long-term sources and sinks of carbon to the atmosphere, we can deduce the level of atmospheric CO_2 at a new time.

This, in a nutshell, is the philosophy of a process-based model of atmospheric CO_2. Process-based models have several advantages over empirical models. By building the model from an understanding of the processes controlling the level of CO_2, rather than factors linked to it through uncertain steps (such as temperature), we become more aware of how well we understand the whole system. We can also compare the results of the process-based model with those of the Energy Balance model. Similar results would give us more confidence in both approaches.

One major problem with a process-based model is that it requires a lot of data. This is why it is impracticable to apply the model to the whole history of the Earth – there are simply not enough data to run the model. Here, therefore, we shall concentrate on the Phanerozoic, for which the pool of evidence is much more secure. An important factor was the explosion of marine organisms with shells which marked the beginning of the Phanerozoic at about 540 million years ago. Hard shells are preserved more readily than soft tissue, so the number and variety of fossils in the record is vast, providing a wealth of information about the environment they lived in (Figure 11.2). Other things become easier as well, for more recently-formed rocks and sediments are better preserved than older specimens, along with the clues they contain about the atmosphere. Thus we have many more tools at our disposal to interpret the evolution of atmospheric CO_2 over the Phanerozoic than over the Cryptozoic.

To use these tools to their maximum effectiveness, we shall follow a similar strategy to that which we employed in Chapter 10 for the Energy Balance model:

◆   assemble what we know about the controlling processes;

◆   substitute things that can be measured for those that cannot;

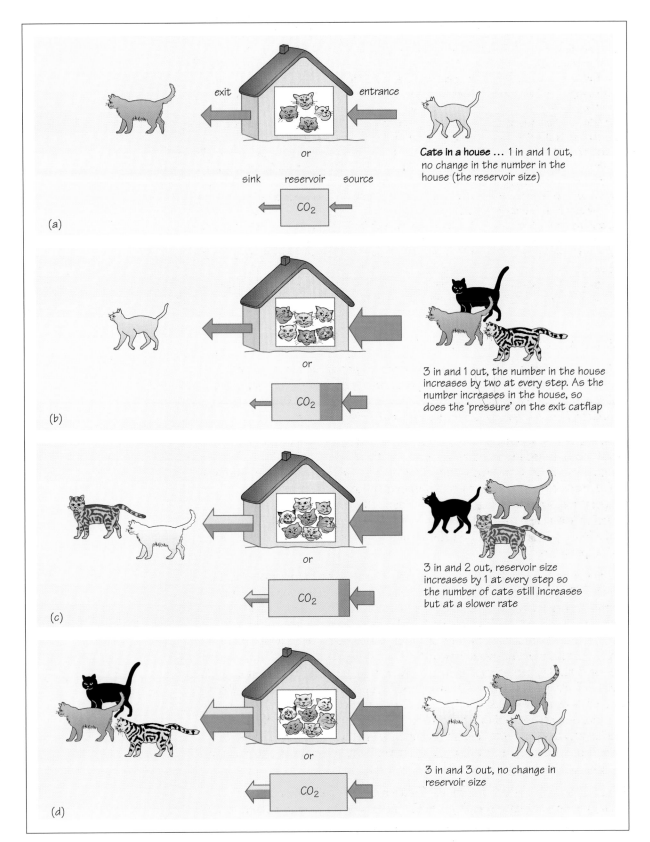

Figure 11.1

An analogy for negative feedback. (a) There is a balance between CO_2 sources and sinks – so the CO_2 reservoir size remains constant. (b) A temporary imbalance between the sources and sinks changes the reservoir size. (c) Negative feedback between reservoir size and source/sink re-establishes the balance, (d) leaving the reservoir size constant again (but changed).

♦ examine our basic assumptions;

♦ formalize relationships into solvable equations;

♦ use these equations to estimate the levels of CO_2;

♦ verify these results where possible by checking the results against independent evidence.

We shall first briefly consider the major sources and sinks for CO_2 (Section 11.2) before considering four propositions about processes taking place during the Phanerozoic (Section 11.3). We then build and evaluate the process-based model in Sections 11.4–11.8.

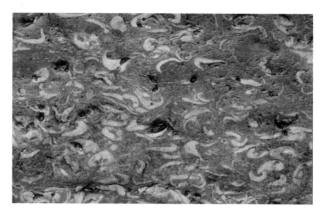

Figure 11.2
Fossilized brachiopod shells in Lower Carboniferous limestone, from Kingsbarns, Fife, Scotland.

11.2 The major sources and sinks of CO_2 to the atmosphere

Long-term CO_2 *sources* take carbon from storage in rock or sedimentary deposits and release it to the atmosphere or surface ocean. Long-term CO_2 *sinks* take carbon from the atmosphere or surface ocean and deposit it in rock or deep-buried sediments. Box 11.2 contains more detail: here we shall just list the main sources and sinks.

The major geological-scale CO_2 *sources* are:

♦ decarbonation and volcanic emission (Figures 11.3 and 11.4);

♦ uplifting and weathering of organic sediments.

The major geological-scale CO_2 *sinks* are:

♦ weathering of silicate rocks on land linked to burial of carbonate carbon in the sea;

♦ photosynthesis linked to burial of organic matter.

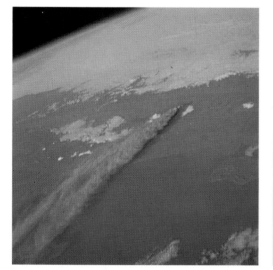

Figure 11.3
Volcanic eruption plume from Klyuchevskaya, Kamchatka on 30 September 1994. Photographed by astronauts aboard the Space Shuttle. The eruption plume of silicate ash particles and volcanic gases (including large amounts of carbon dioxide) extended for hundreds of kilometres over the western Pacific Ocean.

Figure 11.4
Actively outgassing vents at the summit of Stromboli volcano, halfway between Sicily and mainland Italy. These vents have been exhaling a mixture of steam, carbon dioxide, sulfur dioxide and other acid gases throughout recorded history. The geologist in the foreground is the late Richard Thorpe of the Earth Sciences Department, The Open University.

Box 11.2 Carbon dioxide sources, sinks and feedbacks

Major CO_2 sources

1 Decarbonation and volcanic outgassing

Oceanic sea floor is continuously created at mid-ocean ridges and destroyed in subduction zones, and has a mean life span of about 60 million years. In subduction zones, oceanic plates are pushed into the mantle. Here, calcium carbonate ($CaCO_3$) and silicate minerals are heated to high temperatures and pressures and chemically react with each other, liberating CO_2:

$$\text{silicate minerals} + CaCO_3 \longrightarrow \text{`new' silicate minerals} + \underset{\substack{\text{to the} \\ \text{atmosphere}}}{CO_2} \quad \text{(Equation 11.1)}$$

Similarly, carbon sequestered in organic matter in deep-buried sediments can be broken down to gases such as carbon dioxide and methane:

$$2(CH_2O)_n \longrightarrow nCO_2 + nCH_4 \qquad \text{(Equation 11.2)}$$

The process of thermally decomposing carbon-containing rock and sediment, thereby releasing CO_2, is known as **decarbonation**.

The CO_2 and other volatiles produced by decarbonation escape and are ultimately emitted to the atmosphere by volcanoes, hot springs, etc. Volcanoes are the most visual and probably the most dominant form of outgassing from the Earth's interior, exhaling CO_2 from the mantle directly to the atmosphere.

You should note that metamorphism at high temperature and pressure in the crust also releases CO_2 from rocks to the atmosphere.

2 Uplifting and weathering of organic sediments

Deep-buried organic sediments can, over millions of years, become uplifted to the surface during episodes of mountain building. The buried organic sediments are mainly sandstones, siltstones or shales with bits of organic matter dispersed in them. More rarely they are deposits of fossil fuels such as coal seams. Upon exposure to air the sediments can be oxidized by, for instance, burning or microbial breakdown – returning the stored carbon to the atmosphere as CO_2:

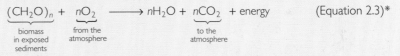

$$\underset{\substack{\text{biomass} \\ \text{in exposed} \\ \text{sediments}}}{(CH_2O)_n} + \underset{\substack{\text{from the} \\ \text{atmosphere}}}{nO_2} \longrightarrow nH_2O + \underset{\substack{\text{to the} \\ \text{atmosphere}}}{nCO_2} + \text{energy} \qquad \text{(Equation 2.3)*}$$

Note that oxidation of an atom of organic carbon (in biomass) uses up a molecule of molecular oxygen.

Major CO_2 sinks

1 Weathering of silicate rocks on land – precipitation and burial of carbonates in the sea

Carbon dioxide in the atmosphere dissolves in rainwater to produce a weak acid, carbonic acid (Equation 9.1). In contact with rock at the surface, the carbonic acid can remove ions such as calcium and sodium from parent minerals – this process is called chemical weathering and it results in the production of bicarbonate ions, HCO_3^-. If the rock is a silicate, the reaction can be simplified as:

$$\underset{\substack{\text{silicate} \\ \text{rock}}}{CaSiO_3} + \underset{\text{carbonic acid}}{2H_2CO_3} + H_2O \longrightarrow \underset{\text{stream/river water}}{Ca^{2+} + 2HCO_3^- + H_4SiO_4} \quad \text{(Equation 11.3)}$$

In shallow seas or along continental shelves, calcium ions released by weathering can recombine chemically with the bicarbonate ions originally from atmospheric CO_2 to form calcium carbonate, a solid deposit:

$$Ca^{2+} + 2HCO_3^- \longrightarrow \underset{\substack{\text{solid calcium} \\ \text{carbonate}}}{CaCO_3} + \underset{\substack{\text{to the} \\ \text{atmosphere}}}{CO_2} + H_2O \qquad \text{(Equation 11.4)}$$

Note that for every two atoms of carbon removed from the atmosphere as CO_2 (Equations 4.2 and 11.3), one atom of carbon is precipitated in calcium carbonate.

Not all rocks are silicates – there are many limestones. But the weathering of *carbonate* rocks is balanced over geologically short times by the precipitation of carbonate in the oceans with no change to atmospheric CO_2:

$$CaCO_3 + CO_2 + H_2O \rightleftharpoons Ca^{2+} + 2HCO_3^-$$ (Equation 11.5)

Reaction 11.4 is mediated by organisms, especially carbonate-secreting plankton which use calcium carbonate for protective shells and skeletons. These plankton occur in both shallow seas and deep oceans. Because of the large area of the world covered by deep oceans in comparison to shallow seas, deep-ocean deposition today is the dominant process globally. Some of these calcium carbonate shells and skeletons settle on the sea floor. Continued deposition can bury these sediments up to several kilometres deep where high pressure and temperatures cause lithification – conversion to rock. The chemical composition of material is not greatly changed but it is physically altered:

$$\underbrace{CaCO_3}_{\text{sediment}} \longrightarrow \underbrace{CaCO_3}_{\text{rock}}$$

The importance of this change is that once the carbon is stored as rock it is effectively removed from active exchange with the sea and atmosphere. Carbonate rock, therefore, is a long-term reservoir for carbon.

2 Photosynthesis and burial of organic matter
Photosynthesis removes CO_2 from the atmosphere (or CO_2 dissolved in water) and stores the carbon as organic matter (plant tissue, including phytoplankton in the ocean):

$$\underbrace{nCO_2}_{\substack{\text{in the} \\ \text{atmosphere}}} + nH_2O + \text{energy} \longrightarrow \underbrace{(CH_2O)_n}_{\text{biomass}} + \underbrace{nO_2}_{\substack{\text{in the} \\ \text{atmosphere}}}$$ (Equation 2.4)*

The net effect of photosynthesis is to lock up carbon in solid organic matter. However, most of this organic matter is returned to the atmosphere in a geologically short time via respiration (Equation 2.3). The organic matter must be stored in long-term deposits in order to have a significant effect on atmospheric CO_2.

Organic matter can be buried and converted under conditions of high temperature and pressure into organic sedimentary deposits. In the ocean, organic carbon in the form of plankton, faecal pellets, and other detritus can become buried in the sea floor and become kerogens, oil, natural gas, etc. On land, trees buried in swamps can be converted into coal or the more diffuse kerogens. The buried biomass on the Earth today contains carbon that quite literally was once part of an ancient atmosphere.

Feedback mechanisms in the global carbon cycle

Changes in the reservoir of atmospheric CO_2 ultimately affect the rate of carbon removal from, or carbon addition to, the atmosphere in a stabilizing negative feedback. Consider, for example, what would happen if the level of atmospheric CO_2 declined. Less greenhouse warming would probably reduce the Earth's surface temperature. Cooler temperatures would mean less evaporation of water and less precipitation, and this combined with less carbonic acid in the rainwater would decrease weathering. Plant growth would also be reduced in a cooler world, with a lower level of atmospheric CO_2. There would be less CO_2 sequestering in plants, and less plant-enhanced weathering (a process described in Section 11.3).

All of the above would reduce the rate of CO_2 transfer from atmosphere to plant to sediments, and from atmosphere to ocean to sediments. But, less CO_2 *removed* from the atmosphere (together with continuing outgassing of CO_2 from volcanoes) would allow atmospheric CO_2 to *increase*. Eventually greenhouse warming would be enhanced again, and CO_2 removal by plants and weathering would increase to match the CO_2 emission. The atmospheric reservoir would be stabilized at a new level by negative feedbacks involving climate and weathering (Box 11.1).

Note that these are only controls operating on a *geological* time-scale, and for this reason do not include carbonate weathering as a CO_2 source or photosynthesis alone as a CO_2 sink. Over the short term (i.e. less than about 1 million years), carbonate weathering balances carbonate precipitation, and photosynthesis very nearly balances respiration. That is, any increase in a short-term carbon source is 'immediately' (on a geological time-scale) translated into an increase in a corresponding carbon sink – so the inputs are never out of balance with the outputs for any appreciable time and atmospheric CO_2 does not change (Figure 11.1). This assumption is justified because the corresponding reservoirs are tightly linked. For instance, if production of plant material (a short-term carbon sink) were to increase in a given year, the reservoir of plant material would increase. Within a relatively short time period, negligible on a geological time-scale, decomposition of the plant material would also increase, so that the CO_2 content of the atmosphere would remain unaffected. Similarly, if more calcium and bicarbonate ions from carbonate weathering were supplied to the oceans, more calcium carbonate would eventually be precipitated.

On the other hand, if significant changes were to take place involving processes linked only over *geological* time-scales, then the CO_2 content of the atmosphere would be affected. For example, if the rates of *burial* of organic carbon in plant matter, or of weathering of *silicate* rocks increased, then the rate of consumption of CO_2 by these sinks would be greater than the supply from sources, since there are no sources linked to either of these sinks that could provide an immediate feedback. Atmospheric CO_2 would decrease until it eventually stabilized at a new (lower) level (Figure 11.1b and c). It is the capability of these sources and sinks to be unbalanced over periods of up to several million years that makes them important for atmospheric CO_2 regulation.

In summary, we shall build our model by simplifying the sources and sinks of atmospheric CO_2 to four processes: volcanism (*source*), weathering of organic carbon deposits (*source*), weathering of silicate minerals (*sink*), and burial of carbonate carbon and organic carbon (*sink*). We shall assume that at various times over the Phanerozoic, imbalances between these sources and sinks caused changes in the level of atmospheric CO_2. As a result of the operation of negative feedback in the system, these sources and sinks eventually reached equilibrium, and the atmospheric CO_2 stabilized at a new level.

11.3 Some propositions about the Phanerozoic Earth

The rate of release and removal of atmospheric CO_2 at any instant is dependent upon the prevailing environmental conditions, such as GMST, global volcanic activity, etc. Evidence from rocks, sediments and fossils is used to reconstruct these environmental conditions over the Phanerozoic. In addition, we can use our knowledge of physics and chemistry to recreate, as far as possible, conditions on Earth over the last 540 million years.

Proposition 1: The Sun continues to brighten
We know that the flux of solar radiation continued to increase over the Phanerozoic. This increase in solar radiation should, all other factors being equal, have increased the temperature of the Earth, which should, in turn, have increased the rate of weathering. (Like most chemical reactions, the rate of weathering is sensitive to temperature.)

▨   Use Figure 10.2 to estimate solar luminosity at the beginning of the Phanerozoic, 540 million years ago.

▨   It was about 95% of today's level.

Proposition 2: Land plants changed the world

Of major importance over the Phanerozoic was the evolution of land plants. Mosses first appeared in the fossil record around 460 million years ago, and by the Carboniferous Period (about 360 million years ago) much of the land area of the Earth was essentially covered by vascular plants (plants with stems and roots). This is crucial to the CO_2 story.

Plants accelerate the removal of atmospheric CO_2 by enhancing weathering in soils. Like all living organisms, plants respire – they take oxygen in through their leaves and release CO_2 – much of it through their roots. Now, plants are usually rooted in moist soil, so the CO_2 released by plant roots dissolves in the soil water, forming carbonic acid (Equation 4.2). This acid then reacts with the minerals in the soil (weathering), releasing ions into solution (Equation 11.3). Plants also secrete organic acids that attack soil minerals and rocks, thereby releasing nutrients for growth. In these ways the leaching of elements from minerals into soil water from land with vegetation is greatly increased over that from bare soil. The weathering reaction (Equation 11.3) itself is not changed by the increase in concentration of the carbonic acid, but the *rate* of weathering is. This produces a negative feedback loop: a high level of CO_2 increases plant productivity, which increases plant respiration, which in turn increases weathering and, therefore, contributes to the removal of atmospheric CO_2. Any CO_2 removed in this way and buried as organic carbon or carbonate carbon is a long-term sink of atmospheric CO_2.

Thus the evolution and spread of land plants in the Phanerozoic greatly enhanced the rates of chemical weathering and therefore of CO_2 removal from the atmosphere. Unfortunately, it is difficult to quantify the global enhancement of weathering by plants. Among other things, the degree of enhancement depends on the type of vegetation, the soil and the prevailing climate. One study in Iceland found a threefold increase in the concentration of weathering-derived ions in water draining vegetated surfaces as opposed to those draining bare ground. Another study in the Swiss Alps found about a sevenfold increase. Overall, though, the data are so scarce and variable that we really don't know the magnitude of the biological enhancement of the global rate of weathering today, much less 400 million years ago.

Proposition 3: Carbonate-secreting plankton changed the oceans

A second significant event in the Phanerozoic was the advent of marine plankton which make skeletons of $CaCO_3$ (Box 11.2). Calcium-secreting plankton fossils first occur in rocks dated at only about 100 million years old. But does the lack of older fossil evidence mean that there were no calcium-secreting plankton before this, or has the record been erased by subduction of the deep-ocean sediments that would have preserved their traces? At present, the consensus is that carbonate-secreting plankton arose about 100–150 million years ago (probably closer to 100 million years). Evolution of these organisms marked a major shift in carbonate deposition from precipitation in shallow water at the edge of continents (both biological and non-biological) to biologically-driven precipitation in the deep ocean. This shift is important for the carbon cycle because sea-floor sediment is recycled far more rapidly than continental-shelf sediment. It takes on average 60 million years to recycle sea-floor sediment by subduction of oceanic plates, while it requires several hundred million years to recycle continental-shelf sediments through uplift and erosion. Thus, carbon stored in deep-ocean sediments returns to the atmosphere (through decarbonation and volcanism) faster than that stored on continental shelves (through uplifting and weathering).

Proposition 4: Continents drift

Over time, the location and relative sizes of the continents has changed due to continental drift. If the continents are clustered near the Equator, weathering, and therefore CO_2 removal from the atmosphere, could possibly be accelerated due to an increase in temperature. Such a 'Ring World' may have existed around 700–600 million years ago, toward the end of the Proterozoic, perhaps triggering the Late Precambrian glaciation. Alternatively, if the continents are primarily clustered around the poles, as was their inferred position some 300–350 million years ago, weathering may have been slowed due to reduced solar radiation, and lower temperature, and therefore the level of atmospheric CO_2 may have increased. Clustering the continents around the poles could also have increased the Earth's albedo if ice-caps were formed, which would have further decreased the Earth's mean surface temperature and decreased global weathering rates.

However, caution must be used in inferring relationships between continent position, weathering rates and levels of atmospheric CO_2. For instance, the position of the continents can strongly affect ocean circulation patterns. A Ring World could allow unimpeded circulation of ocean water from the Equator to the poles, which would set up an efficient transfer of heat around the globe. Warmer ocean water would mean both a warmer planet and one with more atmospheric CO_2, since warm water holds less CO_2 than cold water. Similarly, fragmentation of continents can open 'gateways' where ocean currents can circulate unimpeded by land. Such a scenario probably occurred with the fragmentation of the supercontinent Pangea during the mid-Cretaceous and may have contributed to global warming and enhanced levels of atmospheric CO_2.

We can say in general that the positions of the continents over time has probably affected weathering rates, global albedo, global oceanic circulation patterns, and global mean surface temperature, but the net effect of these on the level of atmospheric CO_2 is highly uncertain. For now we recognize the importance of continental drift but await a clearer picture of its full effect before considering it in a model of atmospheric CO_2.

11.4 Assembling the data and building a model

11.4.1 The data

We have now reviewed the major long-term sources and sinks of atmospheric CO_2, and discussed how they could be modified by particular conditions over the Phanerozoic: increasing flux of solar radiation, evolution of land plants, the evolution of carbonate-secreting plankton, and the changing positions of the continents. We have proposed that measuring the rates of these sources and sinks would allow us to estimate the level of atmospheric CO_2 at any time in Earth's history. Now 'all' we need to do is find a way to measure these rates over time. How are we to go about this?

Clearly we need to use all the tools we have at our disposal – fossils, isotopes, geological deposits, etc. – to give us clues about these rates. For example, we may not be able to measure directly how the rate of volcanic activity on Earth has changed over time, but we can measure the volumes of different volcanic deposits, and date them. Then, knowing the rate at which volcanic activity takes place in different settings today, we can infer what past rates may have been. In so doing, we substitute a process whose rates we *can* measure for one which we *cannot*. These are sometimes called **proxy measurements**.

To build a model of atmospheric CO_2 levels over the Phanerozoic requires quantitative information about the following processes:

♦ the flux of solar radiation;

♦ rates of volcanic activity;

♦ weathering rates of silicate minerals and organic sediments;

♦ the enhancement of weathering rates by the spread of land plants;

♦ burial rates of organic carbon and carbonate carbon;

♦ the effects of the shift of carbonate deposition from shallow continental shelves to deep-ocean basins.

Because there is so much uncertainty involved in estimating these parameters, if we can make estimates of them by using different, independent methods, so much the better.

11.4.2 The GEOCARB model

At this point we turn explicitly to a major process-based model of atmospheric CO_2 over the Phanerozoic. This model was developed over some 10 years by Robert Berner of Yale University and colleagues. Called the **GEOCARB model**, it tests the same assumption that we have proposed: that changes in the level of atmospheric CO_2 result from shifting the balance between long-range processes that add CO_2 into the atmosphere and those processes that remove it. The model breaks up Phanerozoic time into discrete intervals of one million years. It assumes that, overall, the global rate of CO_2 input into the atmosphere over each million-year period balances the rate of CO_2 removal, i.e. the sources and the sinks balance. Disequilibrium between sources and sinks occur, causing the level of atmospheric CO_2 to increase or decrease, but the system readjusts to a new steady state within each million-year interval.

It is important that you are confident that you grasp this essential framework to the model before reading on. If you are uncertain, re-read the start of Chapter 11 and Box 11.1.

For each time interval, the GEOCARB model reconstructs the rate at which CO_2 is added to the atmosphere and the rate at which it is removed due to:

♦ the weathering of silicates, carbonates and organic matter;

♦ the burial of carbonates and organic matter;

♦ the thermal decomposition of buried carbonates and organic matter, with volcanic and metamorphic outgassing of CO_2.

Overall, the model assumes that:

♦ sources and sinks of atmospheric CO_2 balance over time intervals of less than 1 million years;

♦ the variation over time in the factors which control the carbon cycle (and hence CO_2 level) can be expressed as simple equations;

♦ the evidence we find of the changing rates of these controls over time can be related to atmospheric CO_2 levels.

In the following section we shall examine some of the most important data that have been used to estimate the rates of volcanism, weathering and burial of sediments over the Phanerozoic. In Section 11.6 you will take some of these measurements and construct a model with them – which will be an approximation

Figure 11.5
The Hawaiian island chain in the mid-Pacific as seen from the Space Shuttle. (North is at the bottom.)

Figure 11.6
Vertical view from the Space Shuttle of the volcanoes of the Galápagos Islands which are the surface expression of a major 'hot spot' in the Earth's mantle. Several major active volcanoes are visible. Each volcano is about 30 km across.

of the GEOCARB result. You will then compare this approximation with the actual results of the GEOCARB model, and with independent evidence of the level of atmospheric CO_2 over the same time period (Section 11.7). Finally, you will compare for the same time period the results of the GEOCARB process-based model to those of the empirical Energy Balance model (Section 11.8).

11.5 Estimating the controlling processes

11.5.1 Volcanism

Volcanic emission of CO_2 is crucial to the GEOCARB model, for it is the main long-term source of CO_2 from the rocks to the atmosphere. It is self-evidently related to the overall rate of volcanic activity on the Earth. It is likely that this rate has varied over time, but how can it be measured?

One approach is to argue that volcanic activity is related to the level of tectonic activity of the planet. Most volcanoes are formed at plate margins where oceanic sea-floor is subducted beneath continental crust. We can assume that the rate of subduction is proportional to the rate of sea-floor spreading along mid-ocean ridges, because the amount of sea-floor created must equal the amount of sea-floor consumed. If it did not, the Earth would be expanding or contracting. However, over the Earth's history the rate of sea-floor spreading has varied. Times of rapid sea-floor spreading are times of rapid subduction, and times of rapid subduction, the argument goes, are times of high volcanic activity at plate margins. Such times of high global volcanic activity are times of high emission of CO_2 to the atmosphere.

We have some fairly good *direct* methods of estimating the rate of movements of tectonic plates, and thus the rates of volcanic CO_2 emission. One method is to use a fixed 'hot spot' – for instance, a mantle plume, where magma from the mantle breaks through the oceanic crust. Such a source remains fixed as the overlying oceanic plate moves over it leaving a trail, in the same way that moving a sheet of paper over a candle flame will lead to a linear scorch mark.

■   Can you think of an excellent example of this situation?

■   The Hawaiian island chain in the mid-Pacific marks the trace of a 'hot spot', as does the Galápagos island chain (Figures 11.5 and 11.6).

We can measure very accurately the rate at which the Pacific plate has moved over the Hawaiian hot spot – it has moved at about 8.2 centimetres per year over the last 80 million years. Unfortunately, records such as these do not extend back beyond 150 million years (the age of the oldest sea floor). To investigate rates of sea-floor spreading over the whole of the Phanerozoic, we have to turn to *indirect* methods.

Consider Figure 11.7, which is a diagrammatic cross-section of an ocean basin. Mid-ocean ridges, where new sea floor is formed, are prominent topographic features (Figure 11.7a). The mid-Atlantic ridge, for example, extends for thousands of kilometres and rises up some 2–3 km above the surrounding plains: self-evidently, it contains a huge volume of material. During periods of rapid sea-floor spreading, large amounts of new sea floor are formed, increasing the volume of mid-ocean ridges. Increasing the volume of the ridges displaces water, and the water has to go somewhere, so the global mean sea-level rises

(a)

(b)

(Figure 11.7b). (You can think of this as the 'brick in the bath tub' concept.) Thus, the argument goes, if we can measure changes in global sea-level, we can infer changes in sea-floor spreading rates and thus (indirectly) volcanic outgassing.

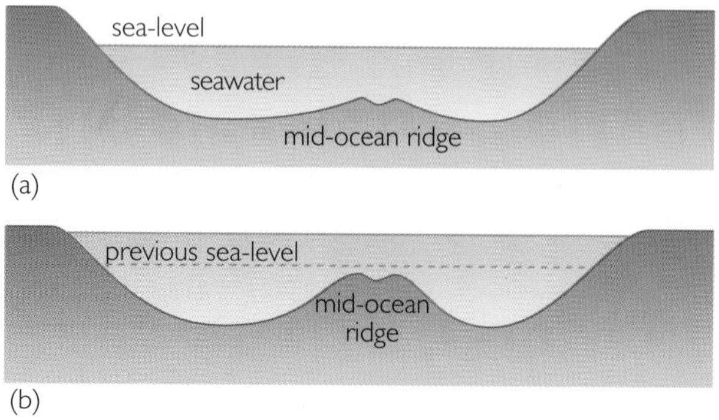

Figure 11.7
Plate tectonics can cause changes in the volumes of ocean basins, and hence in sea-level. (a) An ocean basin with a spreading mid-ocean ridge. (b) An increase in the size of the ridge has caused sea-level to rise.

One problem with this estimate is that the change in sea-level is assumed to be caused by a change in the volume of *the ocean basins* due to tectonic activity. But global sea-level can also change due to changes in the volume of *seawater*. During glacial times, for example, more water is tied up as snow and ice and there is therefore less in the oceans. (One consequence of this is that some 20 000 years ago both the English Channel and the Bering Strait were land – in theory at least you could have walked from London to New York!) Also, *local* changes in sea-level can occur due to vertical land movement. For example, the crust beneath the Mississippi is steadily sinking in response to the huge volumes of sediment deposited on top of it. And in Scandinavia, land is rising in response to the removal of the mass of ice more than a kilometre thick that was present during the last glacial maximum.

Changes in the volume of ocean basins due to sea-floor spreading are assumed to occur over longer time periods than the glacial–interglacial periods, and over wider regions than land areas subjected to vertical movement. So to eliminate these two possible causes of sea-level rise, we would look for evidence of sea-level change over a wide area and over a long period of time. Furthermore, changes in sea-level due to sea-floor spreading (200–300 m in elevation) are generally thought to be potentially larger than changes in sea-level due to other effects. This said, at the last glacial maximum (18 000 years ago) sea-level was probably about 120 m lower than that present today – a large drop. If the present polar caps were to melt, current global mean sea-level would rise by about 80 m. So determining the cause of observed large changes in sea-level is by no means straightforward.

■   If you found evidence that the sea-level had lowered by 200 m at some point in the geological record, how should you go about deciding whether it was caused by glaciation or by declining sea-floor spreading rates?

■   You should look for *independent* lines of evidence for contemporary glaciation, such as extensive moraine deposits.

There is one more potential problem – and it is one of the chicken and the egg – in assuming that the rate of emission of CO_2 through volcanoes can be inferred from past sea-level changes. The global mean sea-level *itself* is related to the global mean surface temperature, since seawater expands as it warms. One of the potential effects of human-induced greenhouse warming is the threat of flooding of our coastal cities: this is partly a consequence of the thermal expansion of water. And of course global mean surface temperature is related to atmospheric CO_2 levels. So a higher sea-level could be either the *direct* result of sea-floor spreading, or an *indirect* result of elevated atmospheric CO_2 through thermal expansion of water due to greenhouse warming.

Fortunately there is a way out of this particular conundrum: the magnitude of the sea-level rise due to thermal expansion, although enough to flood coastal cities, would not approach the hundreds of metres that would occur during major episodes of sea-floor spreading. However, this reminds us that whenever we look at data records, we must take care to distinguish between causes and their effects. With this in mind, turn to the reconstruction of relative sea-floor spreading rates over the Phanerozoic (Figure 11.8). Check that you understand that:

◆ these spreading rates are estimated from both direct measurements (plate movement over hot spots) and indirect relationships (changes in sea-level);

◆ the spreading rates so estimated are assumed to be directly related to rates of tectonic outgassing of CO_2.

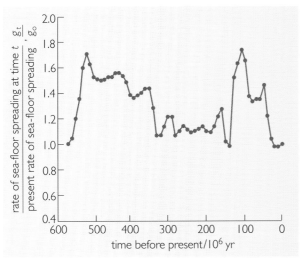

Figure 11.8
Relative sea-floor spreading rates over the Phanerozoic as derived from sea-level estimates. Data are expressed as the ratio g_t/g_o where g_t is the rate of sea-floor spreading at time t and g_o is the rate today.

■ Examine Figure 11.8. Pick out the periods when you would expect the rate of release of CO_2 to the atmosphere to have been high and others where it would have been low.

■ The periods between about 540 and 400 million years ago, and again between 125 and 75 million years ago appear to have been periods of rapid tectonic outgassing, and thus high CO_2 release. By contrast, the period from about 325 to 140 million years ago appears to have been marked by relatively slow tectonic outgassing and therefore lower rates of CO_2 release.

Independent evidence for the more recent of these periods of increased tectonic activity comes from massive Cretaceous lava formations which suggest a large increase in undersea volcanic eruptions started around 120 million years ago. This may have been due to convective plumes formed by overturning of the mantle, and has been termed the mid-Cretaceous **'superplume'** event.

11.5.2 Weathering of silicates

Meaningful estimates of global weathering rates are essential to any process-based model of atmospheric CO_2 levels over the Phanerozoic. These estimates must not only be reliable for a period covering over 540 million years, but they must allow us to distinguish between the weathering of silicate rocks, the weathering of organic sediments and the weathering of carbonate rocks. Weathering occurs when crustal material which had previously been protected in some way from wind, rain, vegetation, and other agents of attack is freshly exposed. One way this occurs is when mountains are uplifted and buried material is exposed as new surface crust.

As you saw in Section 5.5, changes in the rates of continental erosion due to uplifting can be estimated by using the value of the strontium isotopic ratio of seawater: specifically the variation in $^{87}Sr/^{86}Sr$ ratio preserved in marine sediments. The value of $^{87}Sr/^{86}Sr$ in the ocean represents the mixing of the major sources of strontium supplied to the ocean. These come from the weathering of silicates (with a high $^{87}Sr/^{86}Sr$ ratio) and carbonates (intermediate $^{87}Sr/^{86}Sr$) on the continents, and from basalt–seawater reactions at ocean ridges (with a low $^{87}Sr/^{86}Sr$). Periods of rapid weathering of continental silicates, therefore, would be reflected by increased $^{87}Sr/^{86}Sr$ ratios in seawater. This seawater strontium isotopic record can be measured in the shells of marine organisms which were alive at the time and were subsequently preserved in sediments (and later rocks). Measuring the strontium isotopic composition of carbonate rock and sediments of different ages can therefore provide a record of $^{87}Sr/^{86}Sr$ isotopes for the Phanerozoic – such a record is shown in Figure 11.9.

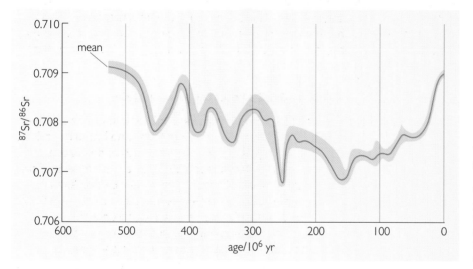

Figure 11.9
The average $^{87}Sr/^{86}Sr$ ratio of seawater over the Phanerozoic as derived from the strontium preserved in marine carbonate deposits measured from sediment cores. The shaded area represents the spread in the original data.

▪ Examine Figure 11.9. Which periods suggest episodes of increased mountain uplift and weathering? And what do these imply about the level of atmospheric CO_2?

▪ Periods of increasing $^{87}Sr/^{86}Sr$ in the record suggest periods of mountain uplift. This appears in several short episodes (i.e. less than 50 million years) between about 450 and 250 million years ago and in a long period beginning around 150 million years ago and continuing to the present. These are likely to have been periods of relatively rapid removal of CO_2 from the atmosphere, as it was used in the weathering of the newly-exposed sediments. Any preservation of this 'extra' removed carbon as organic matter in carbonate rock would be a long-term sink of atmospheric CO_2.

Recall that weathering of carbonate rock has no long-term effect on the level of atmospheric CO_2 (Box 11.2). Weathering of organic sediments has entirely different consequences from the weathering of silicates – it *releases* rather than *consumes* CO_2. Thus, estimates of the proportion of exposed land which is underlain by silicate rock compared to organic sediments at any given time, and the relative rates of weathering of each, must be factored into the estimates of uplift rates to determine the relative importance of each type of sedimentary rock.

11.5.3 Weathering feedbacks

The enhancement of weathering by an increase in the flux of solar radiation can be estimated from the solar luminosity equation (Equation 10.3 and Figure 10.2). This indicates that the amount of solar energy reaching the Earth's surface increased by about 5% over the Phanerozoic. Other things being equal, this increase in solar flux should have led to an increase in weathering rates as a result of increased temperature.

We must also estimate the additional weathering feedback due to the emergence of vascular plants during the Phanerozoic. Although the fossil record is abundant, the magnitude of the feedback of plants on weathering is particularly difficult to estimate. The GEOCARB model assumes that plant-enhanced weathering increases over time from the Silurian (about 440 million years ago) to the present in parallel to the global spread of land plants and the evolution of new families of vascular plants. Vascular plants today are assumed to enhance weathering rates by about seven times over the rate on bare ground. Remember, though, that the data are scarce and variable, and that the magnitude of this biological enhancement of the global rate of weathering is uncertain. It is one of the most problematical aspects of the model.

11.5.4 Sedimentation and burial

The final rate which is required to model atmospheric CO_2 is the rate of sedimentation and burial of carbon, both organic carbon (C_{org}) and carbonate carbon (C_{carb}). Both forms can be deposited either on land or in the oceans. Organic carbon may be deposited in swamps and preserved as kerogens or coal, or it may be deposited in the oceans and preserved in organic sediments, ultimately becoming oil or natural gas in favourable situations. Carbonate carbon may be deposited along continental-shelf areas or precipitated by plankton and deposited in deep-ocean sediments.

Of the major controls on atmospheric CO_2, which we have detailed in this chapter, the rates of sedimentation and burial of carbon are the only ones that can be inferred more or less directly, by using the carbon isotope ratios as described in Section 5.5. The rate of organic carbon burial can also be estimated in another way, by measuring the abundance of organic carbon in different types of sedimentary rocks of different ages. Figure 11.10 shows the results of both estimates: there is broad agreement in the major trends.

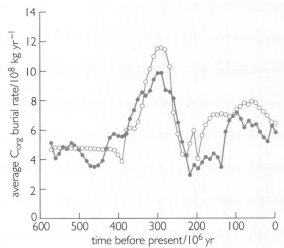

Figure 11.10
Average organic carbon (C_{org}) burial rate over the Phanerozoic. Solid dots: rates inferred from balance of carbon isotope ratios. Circles: rate inferred from the abundance of organic carbon in sedimentary rocks of different ages.

■   Figure 11.10 shows that the rate of organic carbon burial reached a peak about 300 million years ago. From what you know about the major episodes in the Earth's history, can you suggest what this peak might be related to?

■   About 300 million years ago large amounts of plant material were being buried in swamps, which later formed coal deposits.

Although the fact was not appreciated at the time when this period in the geological time-scale was named, the peak organic carbon burial rate occurred in the Carboniferous Period.

11.5.5 Shift of carbonate precipitation from shallow shelves to deep oceans

Over most of the Phanerozoic, carbonate precipitation occurred in shallow seas fringing continents (the continental shelves). However, with the emergence of carbonate-secreting plankton, this locus shifted to the deep-ocean basins. It is important to distinguish between these contrasted sites of carbonate carbon burial. This is because deep-ocean carbonates are returned to the atmosphere through thermal decarbonation reactions as sea-floor subducts at plate boundaries (Figure 10.1). The average period between carbon burial and carbon release via this route is about 60 million years – the average age of the sea-floor before it is subducted. On the other hand, shallow platform or shelf carbonates are not recycled through subduction (Figure 11.11). Their carbon can be released to the atmosphere through metamorphic outgassing or uplift and weathering, but these processes are much slower than the recycling of deep-ocean carbonates – up to an order of magnitude slower. The shift in carbonate deposition from shallow water to deep oceans, then, greatly increased the rate of carbon return to the atmosphere. Unfortunately, we don't really know when that occurred. As indicated in Section 11.3 our best guess is that carbonate-secreting plankton evolved some 100–150 million years ago, and have been increasing in importance since then. The GEOCARB model estimates these two rates and tracks them over time as a ratio.

Figure 11.11
A small vegetated atoll rises above an extensive reef, formed of carbonates deposited in shallow water.

11.6 Bringing the data together

11.6.1 The controlling processes

We can summarize the data we have collected in Sections 11.4 and 11.5 to estimate each of the processes controlling the level of atmospheric CO_2 as follows:

◆ *Rates of volcanic activity* – inferred from sea-floor subduction rates (calculated from fixed hot spots), and changes in ocean-basin volume.

◆ *Weathering rates* of silicate minerals and organic sediments – calculated from estimates of uplift using strontium isotopic ratios, together with estimates of the proportion of silicates and organic sediments weathered.

◆ *Flux of solar radiation* – calculated from the solar luminosity equation, Equation 10.3.

◆ *Enhancement of weathering by plants* – inferred from experimental data and fossil evidence for the rate of colonization of land plants and the evolution of vascular plants.

◆ *Burial rates* of organic carbon and carbonate carbon – calculated from carbon isotope mass balances.

◆ *Ratio of deep-ocean to shelf-sea carbonate deposition* – assumed low and constant until 150 million years ago, then a linear increase to current levels.

In order to calculate the level of atmospheric CO_2 over the Phanerozoic, the GEOCARB model requires 11 equations to be solved for each one-million-year interval, i.e. about 540 intervals. You will be relieved to know that you will not be asked to do this. However, you do not need to solve any equations to get a good idea of the result of the simulation of atmospheric CO_2 levels: you need merely to look back at changes in the factors which regulate CO_2 sources and sinks.

If we turn first to the main sinks for CO_2 (Section 11.2) – silicate weathering and burial of organic carbon – what can we say about how these have changed over time?

◆ The flux of solar radiation has increased steadily throughout the Phanerozoic. Thus, other things being equal, progressively more CO_2 should have been removed over the course of the Phanerozoic due to the resulting increase in temperature and weathering rates.

◆ Land plants appeared about 440 million years ago and rapidly covered the Earth. Weathering is enhanced by plants and so this would have caused further removal of atmospheric CO_2.

◆ A major period of organic carbon burial (and thus atmospheric CO_2 removal) took place between about 250 and 350 million years ago (Figure 11.10).

◆ Strontium isotopic ratios suggest that a major period of continental uplift began about 150 million years ago and continues to the present day (Figure 11.9). This can be both a sink for CO_2 (through the weathering of exposed silicates) or a source (through the weathering of organic sediments). However, it is a much greater sink than it is a source simply because there are many more silicate rocks than lithified organic sediments.

Balancing these CO_2 sinks against periods of increased CO_2 supply are the following CO_2 sources:

◆ Tectonic outgassing of CO_2 was high from about 500 to 350 million years ago, and again from about 125 to 75 million years ago (as estimated from the relative rates of sea-floor spreading, Figure 11.8).

◆ Erosion and weathering of buried organic sediments during continental uplift 150 million years ago would also have enhanced atmospheric CO_2 (as mentioned above). The volume of organic-rich sediments exposed during uplift, however, is much lower than those of silicate rocks.

These periods of enhanced activity of the major CO_2 sources and sinks during the Phanerozoic are shown in Figure 11.12. You should check each of the time-lines in Figure 11.12 with the description above. After it is clear to you what each time-line refers to, you can use Figure 11.12 to make your own reconstruction of atmospheric CO_2 levels over the Phanerozoic in Activity 11.1.

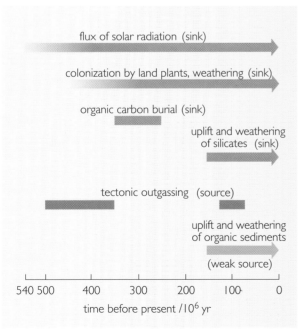

Figure 11.12
Time-line of enhanced activity of the major sources or sinks of atmospheric CO_2 as reconstructed by data on sea-floor spreading rates, fossil and geological deposits, carbon and strontium isotopic data, and other evidence.

Activity 11.1

You should spend a total of about 30 minutes on this Activity.

Part 1

Using the information summarized in Figure 11.12, make a sketch of the qualitative change in the level of atmospheric CO_2 over the Phanerozoic on the blank graph supplied in Figure 11.13. (Alternatively sketch the graph on a piece of paper.)

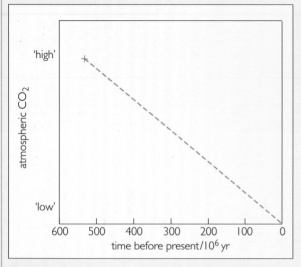

Figure 11.13

Plot for Activity 11.1. The vertical axis denotes the range in atmospheric CO_2 levels over the Phanerozoic from 'higher than average' to 'lower than average'.

We shall start you off with a few tips. First, assume (from Figure 10.8) that the level of CO_2 was higher at the start of the Phanerozoic than its average value over the period. We have marked a starting point for you near 'high' in Figure 11.13 (where 'high' and 'low' refer to the level of atmospheric CO_2 relative to its average value over the Phanerozoic). Next, you can assume that, all else being equal, the level of CO_2 would have steadily declined over the Phanerozoic due to the weathering feedback from the steadily increasing flux of solar radiation (upper line in Figure 11.12). This we have shown as a diagonal line from 'high' at 540 million years ago to 'low' at present.

Against this background there are periods when the level of CO_2 decreased or increased due to fluctuations in different carbon sources or sinks. The estimated time periods of enhanced activity of major carbon sources and sinks are shown in Figure 11.12. *Roughly* sketch how these fluctuations could be interpreted as variations in atmospheric CO_2 level over the Phanerozoic. Aim simply for an indication of trends. You should spend about 5–10 minutes doing this. When you have finished, turn to Figure 11.14 and compare your sketch with the calculated results of the GEOCARB model.

Part 2

Undoubtedly, your rough sketch will differ from the GEOCARB results, because you were not given the actual equations used by the GEOCARB model for the CO_2 sources and sinks. However, your sketch should show the same major *trends* as GEOCARB. A summary of these trends and possible causes for them is given below. From your sketch for Part 1 of this Activity, and Figure 11.14, note down appropriate words or phrases to complete the following statements. (Note that the length of the line used to indicate the missing words is arbitrary.)

1   The overall decline in atmospheric CO_2 over the whole of the Phanerozoic is most likely linked to_____.

2   The increase in the level of CO_2 at about 500 million years ago to its highest level for the whole of the Phanerozoic may have been due to_____.

3   A decline in atmospheric CO_2 from 400 million years ago to 300 million years ago was probably brought on by a lessening of_____and the increase in the sinks caused by_____ and_____.

4   Low levels of atmospheric CO_2 between 350–250 million years ago were related to a major period of _____.

5   An increase in the level of atmospheric CO_2 around 250–125 million years ago may have been due to _____and partly due to_____.

6   A decline in the level of atmospheric CO_2 over the last approximately 125 million years may be due to _____.

11.6.2 Sensitivity analysis

Activity 11.1 illustrates how it is possible to translate the available evidence from the fossil and rock records to a reasonable estimate of the variation in the level of atmospheric CO_2 over the Phanerozoic. You can see that changes over time in the strength of the various sources and sinks of atmospheric CO_2 influence the simulation, and your plot should roughly correspond to the results of the GEOCARB model (Figure 11.14). However, since the GEOCARB model is much more complex, what we have identified as possible sources for variation in atmospheric CO_2 may not be exactly what is simulated in the model. Overall the

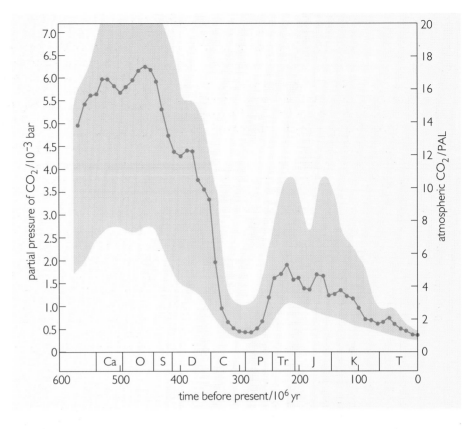

Figure 11.14
Variation in the level of atmospheric CO$_2$ over the Phanerozoic as calculated from the GEOCARB model. Each point on the plot represents model results from calculations at intervals of about 10 million years. The shaded area shows the range of approximate error based on sensitivity analyses. The bar along the bottom axis gives the geological ages beginning with the Cambrian (Ca).

GEOCARB model suggests that the level of atmospheric CO$_2$ has declined from about 2×10^{-3}–7×10^{-3} bar (about 5–20 PAL) at the beginning of the Phanerozoic to the current level of 3.6×10^{-4} bar. We emphasize again, however, that this model is a 'best guess' built on many assumptions and uncertainties – the results help us to examine what we think we know about the controls on atmospheric CO$_2$ but should not be taken as 'absolute truth'.

In order to test the importance of different assumed controls on atmospheric CO$_2$ in the GEOCARB model we can perform a **sensitivity analysis**. In a sensitivity analysis the model is run as usual, but with one (or several) of the processes kept constant (effectively leaving it out of the simulation). The results of these tests are then compared with those of the model incorporating all the processes. Any changes in the results can be then attributed to the missing process(es).

Keeping one variable constant while varying the others in order to test its effect is a good way of testing its importance – the use of this test is not just confined to modellers but is common throughout scientific studies. It is particularly important in complex models such as GEOCARB, where, as we have seen, changes in some processes feed back in complex ways on other processes. Just as the natural world is complex, in GEOCARB it is difficult to tease apart primary controls on CO$_2$ from secondary effects by simply looking at the equations.

You can think of a sensitivity analysis as instructive suspension of reality (even modelled reality!) For instance, we might 'pretend' that land plants never evolved and entirely exclude them from the model. If the estimated atmospheric CO$_2$ changes greatly from that of the original model *with* land plants included, we can conclude that, given our current knowledge on the effect of plants on weathering, the evolution and spread of land plants makes an important impact on atmospheric CO_2. On the other hand, if the level of atmospheric CO_2 does not change much when land plants are left out, we can say that, to the best of our current knowledge, land plants are not as important as other factors for regulating atmospheric CO_2. And if the atmospheric CO_2 level is different only over a limited time period we can identify that period as particularly important for land-plant-mediated controls on atmospheric CO_2.

Sensitivity analysis of the GEOCARB model shows:

- The overall downward pattern of atmospheric CO_2 over the entire Phanerozoic is partly due to the 5% increase in flux of solar radiation over that time.

- This, plus the evolution and spread of land plants accounts for nearly all of the large difference in atmospheric CO_2 between the first half of the Phanerozoic (540 to about 300 million years ago) and the last 300 million years. The effect of land plants, in turn, is sensitive to their enhancement of silicate weathering, which is still poorly understood.

- Apart from the accelerating effect on weathering due to land plants, the steep decline in atmospheric CO_2 during the Carboniferous also reflects increased rates of burial of organic matter.

- Continental uplift (mountain building), of mountain ranges such as the Rockies, the Alps, and the Himalayas, has contributed toward lowering CO_2 levels during the last 65 million years.

- Transfer of carbonate deposition from shallow shelves to the deep oceans throughout the Phanerozoic is an important process which has speeded up the return of CO_2 to the atmosphere. If this had not occurred, modelled atmospheric CO_2 levels would have been lower over the last 150 million years than those shown.

Thus, an important conclusion of the model is that, to the best of our current understanding, the level of atmospheric CO_2 over the Phanerozoic is primarily regulated by changes in solar radiation, land plant evolution, mountain uplift, and the balance of carbonate deposition between shallow and deep water. Or, in Berner's words, 'CO_2 over Phanerozoic time was controlled by a mixture of geologic and biologic processes, combined with a warming sun, with geology dominating at certain periods and biology at others … a purely geologic or purely biologic approach to the long term carbon cycle is overly simplistic.'

11.7 Evaluating the evidence

Like any model, the GEOCARB model sets up a gross simplification of the 'real world' to test our theories about how one part of that world works. However, GEOCARB is more ambitious than most in that it attempts to reconstruct a history of more than 500 million years from evidence that is fragmentary at best. This is reflected in the large error range that goes with the estimates of CO_2 in the model (Figure 11.14). With such ambitious expectations, it is no wonder that GEOCARB has had its share of critics as well as admirers. In this section we shall examine how well the predictions of the model compare with *independent* evidence of atmospheric CO_2 levels during the Phanerozoic. We shall also examine whether the results of the simulation make sense with respect to what we know about ancient climates (or paleoclimates).

11.7.1 Paleosols

In Sections 4.2.4 and 10.7 we reviewed briefly the use of ancient soil profiles, paleosols, to give some constraints to both atmospheric oxygen and CO_2 levels in the Cryptozoic. You may have concluded that estimating the chemistry of the atmosphere from 2-billion-year-old soils is as much of an art as a science. More recently-formed paleosols allow us to estimate atmospheric CO_2 with more confidence.

Thure Cerling of the University of Utah suggested an intriguing way in which paleosols can be used to estimate the atmospheric CO_2 at the time of their formation. Carbon dioxide in soil air and soil water is a mixture: it contains both carbon dioxide that has diffused directly from the atmosphere through the soil pores, and carbon dioxide pumped into the soil through the respiration of plants and bacteria:

$$\text{total } CO_2 \text{ in soil water} = \underbrace{CO_2}_{\substack{\text{from the} \\ \text{atmosphere}}} + \underbrace{CO_2}_{\substack{\text{from plant} \\ \text{respiration}}}$$

For this reason, concentrations of CO_2 in the soil may be as much as ten to forty times higher than in the atmosphere. Carbon isotopes can be used to distinguish between the 'biological' and 'atmospheric' carbon in this soil CO_2. Carbon which has passed through a plant and is released to the outside through plant respiration as carbon dioxide is relatively enriched in the 'common' isotope ^{12}C and depleted in the heavy isotope ^{13}C with respect to the CO_2 in the atmosphere. You can think of it as taking marginally less energy to move the lighter isotope both across the leaf cell membrane during photosynthesis *and* across the root cell membrane during respiration. The $\delta^{13}C$ value of the CO_2 in the soil water is thus the result of a mixture of ^{13}C-enriched ('heavy') CO_2 that has diffused into the soil from the atmosphere, and the ^{13}C-depleted ('light') CO_2 that has been involved in plant metabolism. In other words:

$$\underbrace{\delta^{13}C \text{ of mixed } CO_2}_{\substack{\text{in soil} \\ \text{water}}} = \underbrace{\delta^{13}C \text{ of 'heavy' } CO_2}_{\substack{\text{from the} \\ \text{atmosphere}}} + \underbrace{\delta^{13}C \text{ of 'light' } CO_2}_{\substack{\text{from plant} \\ \text{respiration}}}$$

$\delta^{13}C$ values for the CO_2 released by plant respiration are about $-26‰$, whereas the current $\delta^{13}C$ for atmospheric CO_2 is about $-6.5‰$. Under special circumstances, such as in alkaline desert soils that are temporarily wetted and then dried again, some dissolved inorganic carbon can precipitate out of the soil water to form a solid calcium carbonate ($CaCO_3$) coating around mineral grains. If the soil is preserved as a paleosol, the $CaCO_3$ is preserved with it, trapping with it both atoms of carbon that came into the soil as CO_2 from the atmosphere and atoms that came into the soil through plants. So in theory, $CaCO_3$ formed in soils over any time period should reflect the isotopic composition of the soil water at that time.

It follows that it should be possible to determine the amount of atmospherically-derived CO_2 in the soil $CaCO_3$. Three assumptions are required to achieve this:

- the isotopic 'signatures' (i.e. the $\delta^{13}C$ values for the atmosphere and plants) do not change greatly over the Phanerozoic;

- the amount of respiration-derived CO_2 for each soil of a particular age can be reliably estimated;

- when the level of atmospheric CO_2 is high, proportionally more CO_2 diffuses into soil than during periods when it is low.

The first assumption restricts (for our purposes) the usefulness of this method to periods before about 14 million years ago, when the evolution of a new photosynthetic pathway in some plants changed the carbon isotopic composition of soil CO_2 from plant respiration. The second varies with the age of the soil and the number of samples. Justification for the third assumption, the crux of the argument, comes from some experimental studies.

In theory then, we can measure the isotopic composition of soil carbonate from soils of different ages and, using a model incorporating equations for the diffusion of the CO_2 into soils, estimate the concentration of atmospheric CO_2. Such a model was developed by Cerling and tested by him and others on soils collected from around the world and aged up to 420 million years old.

▪   How would the isotopic composition of soil CO_2 change under conditions of high atmospheric CO_2? How would you expect this to be reflected in paleosol carbonates?

▪   Under conditions of high atmospheric CO_2, the CO_2 mix in soil would be shifted towards 'heavy' atmospheric CO_2 and away from 'light' respiration-derived CO_2. Soil CO_2 would therefore have a heavier isotopic composition. Thus, if soil carbonates are isotopically heavy, one conclusion could be that they formed under a relatively high-CO_2 environment.

There are, as with any model, problems and limitations with this approach. First, the isotopic composition of the soil air may be affected by other factors such as soil temperature, moisture and porosity. Second, plant respiration rates, and therefore the amount of CO_2 derived from respiration, may change as atmospheric CO_2 changes. Also, one must assume that the isotopic signature of both plants and the atmosphere has not changed over time, so that any isotopic shift is due to changes in the proportion of atmospheric CO_2.

Accounting for these assumptions as best as possible, Cerling's model came up with reconstructed atmospheric CO_2 for paleosols based on the $\delta^{13}C$ value of soil carbonates contained within them. These data are summarized in Table 11.1. Note that several samples are measured from each formation, giving a range in the $\delta^{13}C$ measurements for each age. This range in isotopic composition in turn gives a range in estimated atmospheric CO_2. (Note again that this is not the true *error* range, just the range of $\delta^{13}C$ values of the different paleosol samples.) In reviewing this table, keep in mind the many underlying assumptions: the estimates of the level of atmospheric CO_2 should not be accepted as gospel truth!

Table 11.1 Summary of paleosol data taken from a number of sources.

Approximate age of paleosol/10^6 yr	Location of paleosol	$\delta^{13}C$ for the soil $CaCO_3$ (‰) (number of samples given in parentheses)	Level of atmospheric CO_2/10^{-3} bar	Level of atmospheric CO_2/PAL
413	Bloomsburg, South Africa	-5.3 ± 1.2 (9)	3.2–5.2	8.9–14.4
367	Sherman Creek	-9.0 ± 0.1 (5)	9.4–2.1	2.6–5.7
340	Mauch Chunk	-7.0 ± 0.5 (5)	0.61–1.0	1.7–2.8
305	Conemaugh	-7.2 ± 0.6 (8)	0.46–0.79	1.3–2.2
285	Dunkard	-8.7 ± 0.4 (5)	0.14–0.18	0.4–0.5
200	New Haven Arkose, USA	-7.6 ± 1.0 (7)	2.0–3.0	5.6–8.3
120	Spain	-8.4 ± 0.4 (9)	1.6–2.6	4.4–7.2
50	Wyoming, USA	-10.6 ± 1.4 (60)	<0.62	<1.7
14	East Africa	-11.7 ± 1.3 (10)	<0.40	<1.1

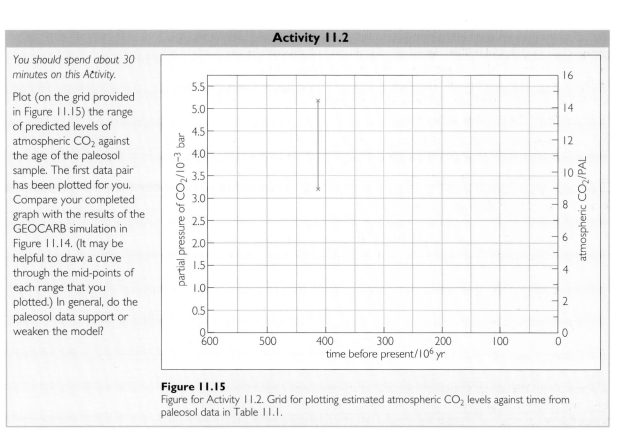

Activity 11.2

You should spend about 30 minutes on this Activity.

Plot (on the grid provided in Figure 11.15) the range of predicted levels of atmospheric CO_2 against the age of the paleosol sample. The first data pair has been plotted for you. Compare your completed graph with the results of the GEOCARB simulation in Figure 11.14. (It may be helpful to draw a curve through the mid-points of each range that you plotted.) In general, do the paleosol data support or weaken the model?

Figure 11.15
Figure for Activity 11.2. Grid for plotting estimated atmospheric CO_2 levels against time from paleosol data in Table 11.1.

You should have found broad agreement between the evidence for ancient atmospheric CO_2 from paleosol data and the modelled GEOCARB results. Like the model, the paleosol data suggest relatively high levels of CO_2 during the early Phanerozoic (about 3.2–5.2×10^{-3} bar or 9–15 PAL), declining steeply to levels in the Carboniferous–Permian (350–240 million years ago) similar to those of today, rising again during the Mesozoic (240–65 million years ago) about 1.5–3×10^{-3} bar (4–8 PAL) and more recently declining in the Tertiary, to levels in the range of about 7×10^{-4} bar (2 PAL).

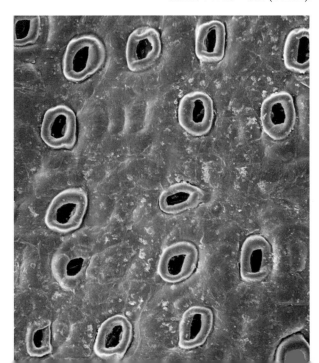

11.7.2 Hungry leaves

Plants take in CO_2 for photosynthesis and release oxygen and water through specialized pores called **stomata**, which can be opened and closed. These are most concentrated on the underside of leaves (Figure 11.16). It has been known for some time that the density of stomata is related to the amount of CO_2 in the atmosphere around the leaf. Plants grown under reduced CO_2 in the laboratory often show an increase in both stomatal density (number of stomata per mm^2 of leaf) and stomatal index (number of stomata per total number of cells on the leaf surface). There is also evidence that some modern forest tree species have reduced stomatal density by 40% in response to rising levels of atmospheric CO_2 over the last 200 years.

Figure 11.16
Scanning electron micrograph of fossil stomata of *Agathis yallournensis* – a conifer-like tree from the Oligocene (34–24 million years ago). ⊢————————⊣
100 μm

The reason for the link between stomatal density and atmospheric CO_2 lies in a trade-off for the plant between taking in CO_2 and losing water. As long as the stomata are open (taking in CO_2 for photosynthesis) the plant is also losing water through the open pores. Therefore, the less time the stomata are open, or the fewer the stomata overall, the better water use efficiency. Under conditions of elevated CO_2 plants can take in the same amount of CO_2 with a lower density of stomata as they do with a higher density of stomata when atmospheric CO_2 is low. The added benefit for the plant is that less water is lost. However, if CO_2 levels decrease, natural selection results in plants with higher stomatal densities, because more pores are needed to take in enough CO_2 for photosynthesis.

Botanists Jennifer McElwain and William Chaloner of Royal Holloway University measured the stomatal index of fossilized leaves from plants which grew in (1) the early Devonian Period (about 400 million years ago) and (2) the late Carboniferous–early Permian Period (around 300 million years ago). They compared their findings to the stomatal index of modern species considered to be their 'nearest living equivalent' (NLE) – species from the present day which are, as far as possible, of comparable ecological setting and structural similarity (since the actual species are extinct today).

McElwain and Chaloner found that the stomatal index of the plants growing around 300 million years ago was not significantly different from that of the NLE species chosen, and inferred that CO_2 levels at that time were not greatly different from today's. In contrast, the stomatal index of the early Devonian plants was about one-sixth that of their modern counterparts. They concluded that their results support the GEOCARB estimates of atmospheric CO_2 being some 10 to 20 times higher during the Devonian than today and declining to near present atmospheric CO_2 levels during the Carboniferous and Permian Periods.

11.7.3 Fussy plankton

Like land plants phytoplankton take in CO_2 for photosynthesis (this CO_2 is dissolved in the seawater) and, also like their counterparts on land, they discriminate in favour of the lighter ^{12}C isotope when photosynthesizing. The extent of the isotope discrimination, however, depends on how much CO_2 is available. If there is a lot of CO_2 in the water, the phytoplankton take in proportionally more ^{12}C over ^{13}C. If there is not so much, the proportion is not so high. As one marine geochemist put it, 'When there's less CO_2 around, the plankton can't afford to be choosy'.

On death, the organic remains of a proportion of these phytoplankton accumulate in marine sediments. These sediments preserve the isotopic composition of the organisms when they were alive. Over time, more sediments can accumulate, forming a record of geochemical conditions over time periods that may span millions of years.

■ Use the logic behind the paleosol method to suggest how a record of carbon isotopic composition in sea-floor sediments can be used to estimate past levels of atmospheric CO_2.

■ If there is more CO_2 in the atmosphere, there will be more CO_2 in the water. This means the phytoplankton will take in more ^{12}C relative to ^{13}C during photosynthesis. So periods of high atmospheric CO_2 should be reflected in a sediment sample as a *lower* $\delta^{13}C$ ratio in organic matter (C_{org}). Conversely, inorganic carbonate (C_{carb}) in the sediment should exhibit a *higher* $\delta^{13}C$ ratio, since it forms in equilibrium with the seawater from which ^{12}C has been preferentially extracted.

A complication arises because the relation between CO_2 dissolved in seawater and atmospheric CO_2 is strongly dependent on the temperature of the water: at any given atmospheric pressure cold water dissolves more CO_2 than warm water. So the temperature of the water at the time the phytoplankton were living must be known. This can be estimated by measuring the oxygen isotope ratios of carbonate deposits of the same age. Factors other than CO_2, such as sunlight or fluctuating nutrients, may also influence the rate of photosynthesis. Each species of phytoplankton may also fractionate CO_2 differently, so changes in the isotopic record may reflect ecological rather than biochemical changes.

Keeping in mind these potential problems with the method, the record of inorganic carbonate (C_{carb}) in marine sediments over the past 140 million years does suggest a higher $\delta^{13}C$ ratio at around 120 million years ago followed by a gradual decline, which is in overall agreement with the GEOCARB model.

11.7.4 Paleoclimate indicators

Paleoclimate indicators of CO_2 rely on the assumption that the Earth's surface temperature is closely correlated with the level of atmospheric CO_2, such that by knowing one, we can estimate the other. We have discussed the assumptions and evidence for this earlier, and have shown how it has been used to recreate the level of atmospheric CO_2 over the Cryptozoic. Clues to climate in the Phanerozoic are extensive, and include oxygen and hydrogen isotopes, geological evidence for glacial deposits and the proliferation of fossils.

We can use our understanding of the climatic requirements of modern species to reconstruct the climate in which their ancestors lived. Some organisms have fairly narrow temperature requirements, and finding them in the fossil record can suggest limits on the temperature at that time. Spectacular finds such as fossilized Mesozoic alligators in modern Siberia clearly suggest a warm humid climate at that time (Figure 11.17). Other clues include physiological traits like the shape of fossil leaves (Figure 11.18) – a preponderance of smooth-leaved plants suggests a warmer climate than a preponderance of toothed-leaved plants.

Land-based fossil information must be coupled with a reconstruction of the position of the continents at the time the fossil was formed. It would be much less surprising to find alligators in Siberia *if* Siberia were located near the Equator at the time (it wasn't though!). We have a good idea of the position of the continents to about 150 million years ago (the extent of the sea-floor paleomagnetic record), and a fair idea back to the early Phanerozoic by matching geological and fossil information from different continents.

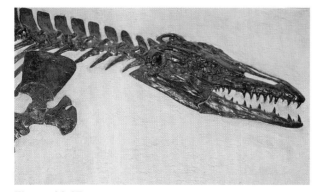

Figure 11.17
Skull and neck of a fossil alligator, *Mososaur*, from the Mesozoic.

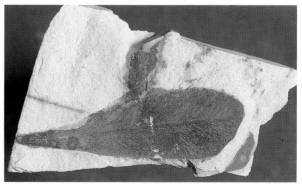

Figure 11.18
Fossil leaf of *Glossopteris* found in New South Wales, Australia, from the Triassic.

Fossils of marine organisms are even more useful in this regard, as the sea averages temperature variations over a wide area. Calcite- and silicate-secreting plankton are particularly informative: because the shells secreted by these organisms are often unique to the species, fluctuations of different populations over time and area can be assessed. Some species are very choosy about the water temperature: the presence of 'cold water' fossils in a sediment core can indicate, for example, nearby glaciers.

Together, all these different types of evidence gives us a good idea of global mean surface temperature over the Phanerozoic which can be used to independently check GEOCARB results. However, GEOCARB gives *atmospheric CO_2 levels* for the Phanerozoic, not temperatures.

▨   How could we estimate surface temperature from the atmospheric CO_2 simulation calculated by the GEOCARB model?

▨   We could use the planetary energy balance equation with an allowance for the greenhouse warming effect of the CO_2 levels simulated by the GEOCARB model.

A plot of global mean surface temperature over the Phanerozoic from fossil and other paleoclimate evidence is shown in Figure 11.19a. You should compare it with the plot of global mean surface temperature derived from the atmospheric CO_2 modelled in the GEOCARB simulation (Figure 11.19b).

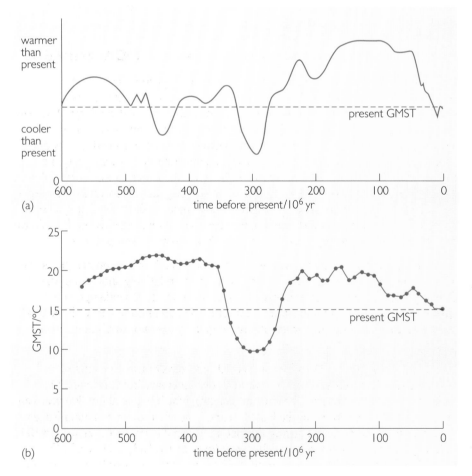

Figure 11.19
Global mean surface temperature over the Phanerozoic as reconstructed by (a) paleoclimate indicators, and (b) the planetary energy balance equation and the atmospheric CO_2 levels estimated by the GEOCARB model. (Present global mean surface temperature is 15 °C.) Note that when you compare the two plots, figure (a) only shows trends in temperature rather than actual temperatures.

There is broad agreement between the independently-derived estimates of global temperature and of atmospheric CO_2 levels over the Phanerozoic. GEOCARB, for instance, suggests a warm climate during the Mesozoic (245–65 Ma ago) and early Paleozoic (540–350 Ma ago) and cool climates during the late Paleozoic (350–250 Ma ago) and Cenozoic (the last 65 Ma). Glacial deposits confirm that there were important glaciations during the Permian and Carboniferous and in the late Cenozoic, at roughly the same time that atmospheric CO_2 and surface temperature dip in the GEOCARB simulation.

There is one important difference, however: the GEOCARB model fails to simulate the Ordovician Ice Age. GEOCARB suggests that CO_2 levels were about 16 times higher than today's atmospheric CO_2 during the Ordovician period some 450 million years ago. This is also borne out by the paleosol evidence (Table 11.1). Temperatures inferred from the GEOCARB model suggest there should have been enough CO_2 to produce a warm Earth, perhaps even a hothouse Earth, but glacial deposits from this time suggest the climate was actually quite different.

Undoubtedly, the paleosol data have large uncertainties that are difficult to quantify. There are also processes (such as ocean circulation) that the model ignores and may need to incorporate. Or, incredible as it may seem, the Ordovician Ice Age may have taken place during a time of warm global mean surface temperature. This is possible if, as seems likely, there were mid-continent climatic extremes during that time, with a large continental mass (Gondwanaland) located in part over the South Pole. It may be significant that the glacial deposits are not that extensive – and the glaciation was probably relatively short, perhaps less than 1 million years in duration.

11.8 Comparing the Energy Balance and GEOCARB models

Figure 11.20a compares the results of atmospheric CO_2 estimated by the GEOCARB simulation with that from the Energy Balance model over the Phanerozoic. There is broad agreement in the overall trend of declining CO_2 due to the 5% increase in the flux of solar radiation over the 540-million-year period. There are also, however, major deviations between the two models due to periods of enhanced volcanism, organic carbon burial and silicate weathering during the Phanerozoic: the GEOCARB incorporates these but the Energy Balance model does not. By both allowing us to test our hypotheses of CO_2 regulation, and by giving a much more detailed reconstruction of the atmospheric levels of CO_2, the process-based model is a more powerful tool than the empirical model. However, for this we pay the price of requiring a large amount of data and much computation.

The trade-off between the two models, then, is between broad reconstructions over a long time period, or detailed reconstructions over a relatively short time period. One approach is neither better nor worse than the other: it depends upon our specific needs. This is an important point for modelling and for science in general. Figure 11.20a illustrates this trade-off by comparing the two simulations on one time-line.

And what of the future? Both ice core records and direct measurements of atmospheric CO_2 levels show a very rapid modern increase in the rate of CO_2 emission to the atmosphere. The current increase, which began about 300 years ago but has greatly accelerated in the last 50 years, is nearly the same in magnitude as the increase which occurred during the last interglacial period centred around 130 million years ago, but at a rate which is *200 times faster*. Only release of CO_2 through human agencies such as fossil fuel burning and deforestation can account for these rates.

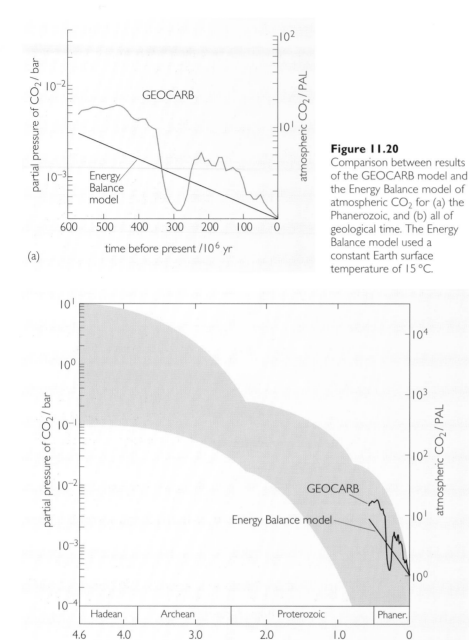

Figure 11.20
Comparison between results of the GEOCARB model and the Energy Balance model of atmospheric CO_2 for (a) the Phanerozoic, and (b) all of geological time. The Energy Balance model used a constant Earth surface temperature of 15 °C.

Levels of atmospheric CO_2 will continue to increase because the rate of fossil fuel production of CO_2 far exceeds the rates at which geochemical processes can remove CO_2 from the atmosphere. Walker and Kasting have estimated that levels of atmospheric CO_2 in the next few centuries could eventually reach up to 0.2% (over 5 PAL) if fossil fuel consumption and deforestation continue at present rates. Levels of atmospheric CO_2 this high have not been seen since the Triassic–Jurassic, or for some 200 million years. This high-CO_2 greenhouse pulse may persist for several thousand years, and traces of human influence on the geochemical carbon cycle could linger for much longer, perhaps of the order of a million years, until the long-term processes of silicate weathering, carbonate deposition and storage and organic matter production and burial have adjusted to the new level.

11.9 Summary of Chapter 11

1   Modelling the level of atmospheric CO_2 over the Phanerozoic is made easier by the abundance of evidence of environmental conditions for that time. This includes a proliferation of shelled organisms in the fossil record, evolution of plants and animals on land, well-preserved sediments, isotope data and buried carbon deposits. These data can be used to reconstruct the long-term sources and sinks of atmospheric CO_2.

2   Results from the GEOCARB model suggest that over the Phanerozoic the atmospheric CO_2 level has declined from roughly 2×10^{-3}–7×10^{-3} bar (about 5–20 PAL) to the current level of 3.6×10^{-4} bar. This decline is due to increased weathering rates from an increase in the flux of solar radiation and the evolution and spread of land plants (beginning about 440 million years ago), burial of organic carbon during the Carboniferous, and mountain building (continental uplift) during the Cenozoic. These were offset by increases in CO_2 sources through tectonic outgassing during the early to mid-Phanerozoic (the period around 540–400 million years ago) and again around 75–125 million years ago.

3   Evidence from carbon isotopes preserved in paleosols and sea-floor sediments generally agrees with the modelled results, as does reconstruction of the atmospheric CO_2 levels from global mean surface temperature changes over the Phanerozoic.

4   Scientists have predicted that in the (geologically) near future, levels of atmospheric CO_2 could reach up to 0.2% (i.e. more than 5 PAL) as a result of human intervention in the carbon cycle over the last several hundred years.

Now try the following questions to consolidate your understanding of this chapter.

Question 11.1
Explain the differences between the weathering of silicate rock, the weathering of organic sediments and the weathering of carbonate rock in terms of their roles as long-term sources or sinks of atmospheric CO_2.

Question 11.2
Evidence for increased levels of atmospheric CO_2 would include an *increase* in the $\delta^{13}C$ ratio of carbonate minerals in paleosols, but a *decrease* in the $\delta^{13}C$ ratio of marine plankton remains. Explain why the same conclusion can be drawn from opposite trends in the $\delta^{13}C$ record.

Question 11.3
Describe how the GEOCARB reconstruction of the levels of atmospheric CO_2 over the Phanerozoic would change if the evolution of land plants were ignored in the model. Discuss two reasons for the differences.

Chapter 12
An overview – the Earth's atmosphere in a lifeless world

12.1 Introduction

This brings us to the end of our review of how the atmosphere, Earth and life have evolved over the last 4600 million years. We have focused on only two of the gases present in the Earth's atmosphere. One of them, oxygen, is a major component of the modern atmosphere; the other, carbon dioxide is not much more than a trace gas. Both of them, however, are equally intimately and inextricably involved with the metabolic processes of life on Earth. Both have also played key roles in the inorganic processes of the evolution of our planet.

Because oxygen and carbon dioxide are so bound up with biological processes (including our own lives), it can be difficult to stand back far enough to perceive their importance in a purely planetary context. One way to place this issue in a sharper focus is to pose the question: what would the Earth, and the Earth's atmosphere, be like if *all* forms of life suddenly ceased to exist? We have seen how the Earth works today, and exhaustively studied the carbon cycle. But how would a completely life-free Earth work? Once again we shall look at the two gases in turn.

12.2 The fate of oxygen in a lifeless world

There would be only a trace of oxygen in the atmosphere of a world in which life had never existed. (A small fraction of oxygen would be continuously formed by photolytic dissociation, but this would be rapidly used up in oxidation reactions.) If life were to be abruptly extinguished on the Earth today, some of the short-term consequences are easily predictable: all the usual sinks for oxygen would continue to consume oxygen, so atmospheric oxygen levels would decline. Some vegetation would be burned in fires; most would slowly rot. In a lifeless world, this would be simple oxidation, rather than a biologically mediated process, as it is today.

■   Would oxidation of all living biomass consume all of the oxygen in the Earth's atmosphere?

■   No. You should recall that there is far more oxygen in the modern atmosphere than can be accounted for by photosynthetic formation of the existing living biomass.

Most of the oxygen currently in the atmosphere can be accounted for through the formation, accumulation and burial of carbon in organic sediments. By definition, these are sealed-off from the atmosphere, and can only be exposed by geological processes of continental uplift and weathering. These are slow processes, so after an initial period of rapid decline when surface vegetation is oxidized, there would be a much longer period during which oxidation of newly-exposed biomass would take place, slowly depleting atmospheric oxygen levels. Similarly, oxygen would also be slowly consumed by inorganic sinks – oxidizing small amounts of reduced gases from volcanoes, and oxidizing traces of reduced iron and sulphides in rocks and sediments newly exposed to the atmosphere by geological processes. Over a period of many millions of years, atmospheric oxygen levels would decline exponentially to an extremely low background level, effectively zero.

■   Would you expect the disappearance of oxygen from the atmosphere to be accompanied by any temperature changes?

■   Without oxygen there would be no ozone. Besides absorbing short-wave ultraviolet radiation, ozone also absorbs long-wave radiation which contributes to the greenhouse effect. So it is likely the surface temperature would be lower if oxygen were to disappear from the atmosphere (see Section 10.5.4).

Of course, our lifeless world would ultimately end up ozone-free as well as oxygen-free, with a massive increase in the ultraviolet flux reaching the surface. In the absence of life, however, this issue would be of little consequence. Because atmospheric oxygen is the product of biological activity, the ultimate disappearance of oxygen from a lifeless world is uncontroversial. The *rate* at which it disappeared, however, would be regulated by the rates of geological processes of uplift and weathering. These are more difficult to pin down.

12.3 The fate of carbon dioxide in a lifeless world

There is much less carbon dioxide than oxygen in the present-day atmosphere, but its fate is more complicated because it has both organic and inorganic sources. In the short term, the demise of life would lead to an increase in atmospheric carbon dioxide, as oxidation of newly dead biomass returned carbon to the atmosphere. This would be a one-for-one exchange: every atom of oxidized biomass carbon would consume one molecule of oxygen and liberate one molecule of carbon dioxide. Once all the surface (dead) biomass had been oxidized, the rate of atmospheric CO_2 increase would slow, but would continue as geological processes exposed rocks and sediments to weathering. As atmospheric carbon dioxide levels rose, more would be partitioned in the oceans.

■   What would be the immediate implication of increasing atmospheric CO_2?

■   There would be an enhanced greenhouse effect, and an increase in global mean surface temperature.

You should also have spotted that increasing atmospheric CO_2 has a negative feedback effect: as temperatures rise, so weathering of silicate rocks by carbonic acid in rainfall increases, depleting the atmosphere in carbon, and removing it to the oceans.

In our modern Earth, biological activity is a major sink for carbon dioxide, both on land and in the oceans. Over the long term, atmospheric CO_2 levels would tend to increase as buried carbon deposits were exposed and oxidized, and as volcanism continued to pump the gas into the atmosphere. Some would be derived directly from the mantle; some would be derived by decarbonation of subducted sediments at plate margins. Over the very long term – tens of hundreds of millions of years – the effects of several hundred million years worth of biological activity in sequestering carbon from the atmosphere would be slowly undone. Instead of being characterized by nitrogen and oxygen, the Earth's atmosphere would be characterized by nitrogen and carbon dioxide.

Inevitably, therefore, surface temperatures would rise in response to the enhanced carbon dioxide greenhouse effect. And at some point, which is difficult to predict, a 'runaway greenhouse effect' like that on Venus would cause the oceans to vaporize. This seems to be the inevitable fate of the Earth, whether or not life is abruptly extinguished as in our 'thought experiment'. It is the Sun which ultimately holds the key to the Earth's fate: as its luminosity slowly increases, Earth's surface temperature is bound to rise until the oceans vaporize. The evolution of life has slowed down this warming by sequestering carbon from the atmosphere, and for the foreseeable future biological processes will stave off the runaway greenhouse. But it will happen.

Now try the following questions to consolidate your understanding of this chapter.

Question 12.1
Are there any feedback processes that would work to slow the rate of decline in the level of oxygen in a lifeless world?

Question 12.2
On a lifeless Earth, the effects of biological activity in sequestering carbon from the atmosphere would be slowly undone. But would these effects inevitably be completely undone? If not, why not

Objectives

When you have finished this book, you should be able to display your understanding of the terms printed in **bold** type within the text as well as the following topics, concepts and principles and, where appropriate, perform simple calculations related to them:

1   the components of the Earth System that lead to the production of oxygen by photosynthesis and its accumulation in the atmosphere by burial of organic carbon;

2   the mass balance relationships between the various components of the Earth System related to oxygen formation and organic carbon burial;

3   the nature of oxidation, reduction, combustion and respiration and their roles in the Earth System;

4   the main lines of evidence for atmospheric oxygen levels inferred from the both the fossil and rock records;

5   the likely stages in the evolution of the Earth's early atmosphere;

6   the role of carbon isotope evidence for photosynthesis on the early Earth and the inferences that can be drawn about the rates of organic carbon burial over geological time;

7   the key parameters used in the Berner and Canfield model for Phanerozoic oxygen levels;

8   some of the possible implications for life of elevated oxygen levels during the Phanerozoic;

9   some of the hypotheses advanced to account for the apparent regulation of atmospheric oxygen levels over the Phanerozoic, particularly the role of phosphorus;

10 the links between oxygen and ozone, and the importance of ozone in the stratosphere as a screen for ultraviolet radiation both at the present day and in the early Earth with lower atmospheric oxygen levels;

11 the major differences between empirical and process-based models, by reference to the Energy Balance model and GEOCARB model for atmospheric carbon dioxide levels;

12 the contrast between the major carbon sinks occurring today and those presumed to have operated in the Hadean Earth;

13 the three major assumptions of the Energy Balance model and the evidence that can be used to test each assumption;

14 the important differences between short-term and long-term sources and sinks of atmospheric carbon dioxide with respect to their effects on the level of atmospheric carbon dioxide;

15 the use of proxy measurements in estimating, for the GEOCARB model, the rates of (1) volcanism, (2) silicate weathering, (3) enhancement of weathering by plants, and (4) burial of organic and carbonate carbon;

16 the main lines of independent evidence for atmospheric carbon dioxide levels over time from the fossil and rock records, and how well or poorly the evidence fits (1) the Energy Balance CO_2 model, and (2) the GEOCARB model.

Answers to Questions

Question 2.1

The mass of the atmosphere is 5.3×10^{18} kg. Of this, 0.036% (by volume) is carbon dioxide. The relative molecular mass of carbon dioxide is 44, so the mass of carbon dioxide in the atmosphere is:

$$5.3 \times 10^{18}\,\text{kg} \times 3.6 \times 10^{-4} \times (44/29) = 2.9 \times 10^{15}\,\text{kg}$$

Therefore there is roughly 500 times as much oxygen as carbon dioxide (by mass) in the atmosphere.

Question 2.2

Burial of one unit of biomass (containing one atom of carbon) liberates one unit of molecular oxygen. The relative atomic masses of carbon and oxygen are 12 and 16, respectively. Thus for every kilogram of carbon buried, $(32/12)$ kg of oxygen will accumulate in the atmosphere.

Therefore, if 1.2×10^{11} kg of organic carbon are buried each year, $1.2 \times 10^{11} \times (32/12)$ kg $= 3.2 \times 10^{11}$ kg of oxygen will accumulate each year.

Question 2.3

One factor is simply the area of the Earth that is available for plants to grow. This is limited by the amount of land area with a suitable temperature and water supply. A second factor is the rate of supply of energy (from the Sun) and of nutrients such as phosphorus. This is true of both land and marine growth, although marine biomass is more regulated by nutrient supply than land biomass, which is itself more sensitive to climatic factors. Finally, the amount of plant biomass in existence at any one time will also be limited by the rate at which it is consumed by heterotrophs.

Question 3.1

One would expect that the burial of organic carbon (in the form of biomass) would lead to an *increase* in atmospheric oxygen. The situation is more complex, as we shall see, because whether or not atmospheric oxygen increases depends on the overall rate of carbon burial from *all* sources worldwide. Although we have a good inventory of coal deposits, we have much less idea of how much carbon was – *or was not* – being buried in other reservoirs.

Question 3.2

Not necessarily – even if there were a huge increase in the amount of living biomass, as there may have been when forests covered the land, the isotopic character of the C_{org} and C_{carb} reservoirs would still be controlled by the amount of organic carbon being *buried*. This is not directly controlled by the amount of biomass, but by the processes that lead to burial of carbon. These are essentially geological. $\delta^{13}C$ values in the C_{carb} reservoir could only change if large amounts of ^{12}C fixed as organic carbon in biomass by photosynthesis were to be buried in sediments. Because it is smaller, the C_{org} reservoir would reveal changes more easily than the C_{carb} reservoir.

Question 3.3
As emphasized in Question 3.2, the essential point is that it is not just the amount of photosythesizing plant material that influences atmospheric oxygen contents, but *the rate of organic carbon burial.* If the evolution of trees and other land plants influenced atmospheric oxygen levels, it was because the evolution of woody materials provided new and efficient means of burying organic carbon in sediments.

Question 3.4
There is no easy answer to this question, since the predators themselves would also, of course, be part of the living biomass.

Question 4.1
Table 4.1 shows that 4×10^{14} tonnes (i.e. 4×10^{17} kg) of BIFs were deposited between 2.5 and 2.2 billion years ago. Of this mass, 30% is Fe_2O_3. Thus, 4×10^{17} kg $\times 0.3$, or 1.2×10^{17} kg of Fe_2O_3 were deposited.

The relative atomic masses of oxygen and iron are 16 and 56, respectively, so the relative molecular mass of Fe_2O_3 is $(2 \times 56) + (3 \times 16) = 160$. Therefore the amount of oxygen incorporated in the BIF deposits is $(48/160) \times 1.2 \times 10^{17}$ kg $= 3.6 \times 10^{16}$ kg.

It is likely that the oxygen bound up in the BIFs was a fairly significant proportion of that present in the atmosphere at the time. Bear in mind that the atmosphere with 21% of oxygen by volume contains 1.2×10^{18} kg of molecular oxygen.

Question 4.2
A 1 mm layer in a 200 km circular basin will have a volume of

$$10^{-3}\,\text{m} \times \pi \times (10^5\,\text{m})^2 = 3.14 \times 10^7\,\text{m}^3$$

If this layer is of pure haematite, it will have a mass of

$$3.14 \times 10^7\,\text{m}^3 \times 5.5 \times 10^3\,\text{kg m}^{-3} = 1.73 \times 10^{11}\,\text{kg}$$

Each molecule of haematite contains three oxygen atoms. The relative molecular mass of Fe_2O_3 is 160, so the amount of oxygen in 1.73×10^{11} kg of haematite is

$$(48/160) \times 1.73 \times 10^{11}\,\text{kg} = 5.19 \times 10^{10}\,\text{kg}$$

Now in Section 2.4, we saw that for every unit of biomass produced (relative molecular mass 30) one molecule of molecular oxygen (relative molecular mass 32) was released. Therefore $(30/32) \times 5.19 \times 10^{10}$ kg $= 4.86 \times 10^{10}$ kg of biomass would have been produced as the oxygen contained in the BIF layer was initially generated.

There are about 3×10^{12} kg of living biomass in the oceans today, so it is plausible that photosynthesis could have supplied the oxygen required to make the BIFs.

Question 4.3
They could certainly form today, but they would not go 'critical' because the deposits would be depleted in ^{235}U. Radioactive ^{235}U would have constituted a far higher proportion of the uranium present when the Oklo deposits formed than is the case in modern deposits.

Question 4.4

The rock record is incomplete, especially in the case of very ancient rocks and therefore any evidence taken from it should be treated with caution. The *apparent* absence of some feature may merely mean that no record of that feature has been *preserved*.

Question 4.5

Although the *total* iron contents of the rocks are the same, the ratio of ferrous iron (FeO) to ferric iron (Fe_2O_3) may be very different. In a rock with a high ferrous iron content, the small amount of dissolved oxygen in the rainwater would be rapidly used up in oxidizing the ferrous iron to ferric iron, leaving substantial amounts of ferrous iron to be removed in solution. Thus the soil would have less ferrous iron, and less total iron than the source rock. In a rock with a high ferric iron content, the ferric iron would remain insoluble, so less leaching would take place and the iron content of the soil would remain similar to that of the source rock.

Question 5.1

Figure A1 shows the variation in the amount of ^{40}Ar and ^{129}Xe in the mantle over time if there had been a major outgassing event 2 billion years ago (a *hypothetical* situation). By this time all the ^{129}I would have decayed to ^{129}Xe, so the ^{129}Xe would have been at its maximum value, and the ^{40}Ar levels would have been slowly increasing. During the outgassing event *all* the ^{129}Xe and ^{40}Ar present would have been expelled from the mantle – so both values would have been set back to zero. As there would have been no parent isotope left, the ^{129}Xe would never reappear, but the level of ^{40}Ar would start to increase once more as the radioactive decay of ^{40}K continued.

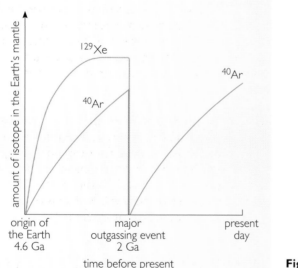

Figure A1
Answer to Question 5.1.

Question 5.2

Sunlight interacts with oxygen in the upper atmosphere to produce a protective shield of ozone (O_3). Ozone is also produced near the ground by photochemical reactions between sunlight and chemicals in traffic fumes, generating an unpleasant brownish smog, especially in large cities such as Los Angeles.

Question 5.3

The oxygen level on the early Earth could not rise until the large inorganic sinks for oxygen, such as the ferrous (reduced) iron supplied by mid-ocean hydrothermal vents, had been soaked up. BIF formation used up a lot of oxygen. Additionally, while ancient sediments contain about 0.5% organic carbon, it is the *total* mass of this organic carbon in them that influences atmospheric oxygen levels. Geological processes of continental growth, rifting, mountain building and erosion enhance the rate of sediment burial, and hence increase the total mass of buried carbon, permitting the atmospheric oxygen level to increase.

Question 5.4

This can be answered by inserting the appropriate values in Equation 5.6:

$$f_{org} = \frac{\delta^{13}C_{in} - \delta^{13}C_{carb}}{\delta^{13}C_{org} - \delta^{13}C_{carb}}$$

We are told that $\delta^{13}C$ for carbonate carbon that entered the Earth's environment was 0‰, and for organic carbon was −45‰. Thus:

$$f_{org} = \frac{-5 - 0}{-45 - 0} = \frac{-5}{-45} = 0.11$$

So about 0.11, i.e. about 11%, of the total carbon that entered the Earth's environment was deposited was organic carbon.

Question 5.5

The percentage of *organic* carbon in any sediment is simply the proportion of the sediment that consists of organic carbon; the remainder may be carbonate carbon, or some mixture of carbonate carbon and silicates in the form of sand, muds and clay. The fraction of organic carbon in the sediments describes the *proportion* of the organic carbon to the total mass of crustal carbon alone. It takes no account of the amounts of silicate muds, clays etc., so it is not related to the concentration of carbon in the sediments. The fraction of organic carbon can only be deduced by measuring the isotopic compositions of both organic and carbonate carbon.

Question 5.6

A higher $\delta^{13}C$ value implies that carbonate carbon enriched in ^{13}C must have been formed from an atmosphere that was depleted in ^{12}C. This could *only* happen if ^{12}C was concentrated preferentially by photosynthesis into organic carbon in living matter, *and* if that organic carbon was then sequestered in sediments. Enhanced burial of organic carbon yields an increase in atmospheric oxygen levels. The enhanced organic carbon burial rate suggested by the new $\delta^{13}C$ data is consistent with Figure 5.3, although the peak in f_{org} occurred slightly earlier in Earth's history.

Question 6.1

In qualitative terms, doubling the world weathering rate of pyrite, F_{WS}, would increase the term $[F_{WC} + (15/8)F_{WS}]$ on the right-hand side of Equation 6.1. This would result in a decrease in R_O on the left-hand side of the equation. In other words, the rate of increase in the oxygen level would fall, i.e. the rate of increase would slow down. If the value in brackets became larger enough, the right-hand side of the equation would become negative which would mean that the oxygen content of the atmosphere would be *decreasing* with time.

Question 6.2
Birds are major predators of modern dragonflies. Birds had not evolved at the time when the giant dragonflies flourished, so it possible that this absence of predation, rather than elevated oxygen levels, permitted dragonflies to reach large sizes. A large, slow-flying dragonfly would be easy meat for the equivalent of a modern hawk or eagle.

Question 6.3
Because CO_2 has a significantly higher relative molecular mass (44) than O_2 (32), the density of the atmosphere would be higher than that today. (Note: the relative molecular masses of oxygen and nitrogen are quite close, so we were able to ignore this difference in the discussion in Section 6.5.) Of course, such a high CO_2 level would also cause a massive greenhouse effect, driving temperatures very high. This, in turn, would affect the atmospheric pressure and density.

Question 6.4
Birds have lungs, but insects do not. Therefore birds can 'burn' their energy source (food) far more efficiently than insects and so have more power available. This extra power has enabled larger birds to evolve. (The pioneering aviators, Orville and Wilbur Wright succeeded where others had failed partly because they were able to build a lighter, more efficient engine.)

Question 7.1
According to Lovelock's argument, if oxygen levels were to fall, forest fires would be suppressed. This would favour the growth of hardwood trees, which are less tolerant of fires than softwoods. Hardwoods contain more lignin and produce more charcoal when they burn, thus more organic carbon would be buried, and in due course atmospheric oxygen levels would rise.

Question 7.2
At equilibrium, the rate of oxygen input must be the same as the rate of oxygen output. Thus, the oxygen input must also be 5×10^{11} kg yr^{-1}. We can see from Figure 7.2 that this rate of oxygen input occurs at an atmospheric oxygen level of about 2–3%.

Question 7.3
Prior to about 2.2 billion years ago, atmospheric oxygen levels were extremely low. In one sense, they could be said to be stable, because they were so low. This situation prevailed because the preponderance of inorganic sinks prevented atmospheric oxygen levels from rising even though oxygenic photosynthesizers were producing oxygen at that time.

Question 7.4
Simply increasing the total amount of marine biomass would have little direct effect on atmospheric oxygen levels – it is the amount of organic carbon that gets buried in the sediments that matters.

Question 8.1
Ultraviolet radiation seems to provide an absolute constraint on the existence of life. This is probably due to the fact that ultraviolet radiation damages DNA, the molecular basis of all life. While desert plants have evolved mechanisms for reducing their exposure to longer wavelength ultraviolet, they, and all other plants, are still vulnerable to shorter wavelengths. No plants have been able to evolve strategies to protect themselves from shorter wavelength ultraviolet radiation.

Question 8.2
If the observed variations were *wavelength dependent* as shown in Figure 8.6, then they would suggest variations in ozone abundance. Far less ultraviolet is transmitted at shorter wavelengths than at longer wavelengths – the light incident (the flux) on the Earth at $0.300\,\mu m$ is only 1% of that incident at $0.324\,\mu m$.

Question 10.1
Today, the major carbon sinks are land-based weathering of silicate minerals combined with sea-floor deposition of carbonate, and organic carbon fixation through photosynthesis combined with storage of organic carbon by sedimentation and burial. During the Hadean, when there were no land masses, scientists believe that dissolved inorganic carbon was primarily removed by carbonation reactions in mid-ocean hydrothermal vents. This is only a minor removal mechanism (sink) on Earth today. The major site of carbon storage in the Hadean was probably ocean sediments; today it is the calcium carbonate deposits initially formed in the sea, which through uplifting are today stored on land.

Question 10.2
Since changing solar luminosity is the crucial variable in the Energy Balance model, the level of atmospheric CO_2 would not have to decrease in order to maintain the desired temperature if the luminosity had remained at 30% of its present value: it would remain at the initial level, i.e. between 7 and 0.1 bar (13 000 and 280 PAL). Evidence of carbonation reactions and burial of organic carbon beginning from the Archean, as well as paleosol evidence from as far back as 2.7 billion years ago, would indicate that such levels of atmospheric CO_2 are unrealistically high and that large sinks for carbon developed over the Archean and Proterozoic.

Question 10.3
This paleosol evidence indicates a *lower* level of atmospheric CO_2 than the Energy Balance model predicts, suggesting that the assumptions made in the model need to be modified or refined. These may include the assumptions that greenhouse gases other than CO_2 did not play a major role in climate control in the early history of the Earth, or that other climatic conditions (e.g. cloud cover) were similar to those present today.

Question 11.1
Weathering of silicate rock combined with carbonate precipitation is a long-term *sink* of atmospheric CO_2, because more carbon is removed from the atmosphere during weathering than is later returned to the ocean/atmosphere system during carbonate precipitation. Weathering of organic sediments through oxidation is a *source* of atmospheric CO_2 as organic carbon stored in sediments is combined with atmospheric oxygen to form carbon dioxide. Weathering of carbonate rock is neither a long-term source nor sink of atmospheric CO_2 because the same amount of carbon removed from the atmosphere to weather the rock is later returned to the surface ocean/atmosphere system during carbonate precipitation.

Question 11.2
Both land plants and plankton preferentially take up the lighter carbon isotope ^{12}C. The difference in the interpretation of the isotopic data is that the plankton data directly reflect the carbon fixed by photosynthesis while the paleosol data reflect a mixture of the carbon fixed by plants and the carbon diffused directly from the atmosphere. During periods of high levels of atmospheric CO_2 this ratio shifts

towards carbon diffused from the atmosphere, that is 'heavier' carbon, not fixed by photosynthesis. Therefore, we look for opposite trends in the $\delta^{13}C$ signature.

Question 11.3

In the absence of land plants, the decline in estimated atmospheric CO_2 from about 450 million years ago would have been much more gradual, reflecting only inorganic weathering processes rather than plant-accelerated enhancement of this weathering and organic carbon burial. The low levels of CO_2 present during the Carboniferous and Permian would also not have been reached. Major reasons for the differences are therefore (1) a lack of enhancement of weathering by plants, and (2) a decrease in the production and burial of organic matter.

Question 12.1

Not really. Any feedback mechanism would require that declining atmospheric oxygen levels enhanced productivity in a source. Since the only (significant) sources of oxygen are of biological origin, on a lifeless world there would be no possibility of enhanced oxygen production.

Question 12.2

It is unlikely that all of the carbon sequestered from the atmosphere would eventually be returned there. This is because a proportion of it is locked up in carbonate rocks of the continental crust. The existence of stromatolites more than 3 billion years old demonstrates that not all biogenic carbonates get recycled.

Comments on Activities

Activity 3.1

Your completed summary table recording the changes in atmospheric oxygen levels over geological time, should be similar to Table A1.

Table A1   Atmospheric oxygen levels deduced from the fossil record. Activity 3.1.

Age or age range	Atmospheric oxygen as a percentage of the total atmosphere	Atmospheric oxygen as a fraction of the present atmospheric level, PAL
present day	21%	1.0 PAL
380 Ma to present day	21%	1.0 PAL
400 Ma to present day	21%	1.0 PAL
about 300 Ma	15–30%	0.7–1.4 PAL
about 580 Ma	1–2%	0.05–0.1 PAL
2100 Ma	0.2%	0.01 PAL

You should not take these values as necessarily authoritative – they could well be changed in the future as various models are refined, or our knowledge of the early rock record improves.

Activity 10.1

The completed table is given in Table A2.

Table A2   Completed Table 10.1 for Activity 10.1. Estimated mean atmospheric CO_2 levels over geological time.

Age/10^9 yr	Mean minimum level of atmospheric CO_2	Mean maximum level of atmospheric CO_2
4.6	0.1 bar	7 bar
2.3	3.3×10^{-2} bar	2×10^{-1} bar
0.8	2×10^{-4} bar	2.5×10^{-2} bar
present day	3.6×10^{-4} bar	3.6×10^{-4} bar

By answering this Activity you have demonstrated how an empirical model of the change in atmospheric CO_2 levels over time can be built up by using simple principles of global energy balance. The range in estimated global mean surface temperature over the two Ice Ages gives a range for estimated atmospheric CO_2 via the Energy Balance model. Your answer should show estimated atmospheric CO_2 levels declining from 2.3 billion years ago to 0.8 billion years ago. If you had estimates of global mean surface temperature from other time periods in the Cryptozoic, you could use the Energy Balance model to calculate atmospheric CO_2 for these periods – and so build the model. Kasting does so – his full model output is shown in Figure 10.8.

Activity 11.1

Part 1

In doing this Activity you have demonstrated how a process-based model of atmospheric CO_2 levels over time can be built up by using proxy data for the rates of major CO_2 sources and sinks. By following the information summarized in Figure 11.12, your sketch should show relatively high atmospheric CO_2 levels from about 500 to 400 million years ago due to tectonic outgassing, and then a fairly strong decline beginning around 350 million years ago as land plant colonization and organic carbon burial, two strong sinks, become important. By 250 million years ago the period of greatly enhanced organic carbon burial ended – and thus your sketch should show atmospheric CO_2 beginning to increase again. The period from about 150 million years ago to the present should show a general decline in atmospheric CO_2 levels due to the uplift and weathering of silicate rocks – a strong sink. This decline might have a small 'bump' of increased atmospheric CO_2 around 100 million years ago due to a period of enhanced tectonic activity.

When comparing your results to that of GEOCARB (Figure 11.14) you should see that you have captured the essence of the model's reconstruction – and have avoided having to solve several thousand equations! Differences between your sketch and GEOCARB reflect, in part, complicated interactions in which several sources and sinks are acting at the same time – atmospheric CO_2 levels reflect the net sum of the different rates of these processes, which you cannot show in your rough sketch.

Part 2

The completed statements are as follows:

1   The overall decline in atmospheric CO_2 over the whole of the Phanerozoic is most likely linked to *a 5% increase in the flux of solar radiation.*

2   The increase in the level of CO_2 at about 500 million years ago to its highest level for the whole of the Phanerozoic may have been due to *enhanced tectonic outgassing.*

3   A decline in atmospheric CO_2 from 400 million years ago to 300 million years ago was probably brought on by a lessening of *tectonic outgassing* and the increase in the sinks caused by *land plant evolution* and *organic carbon burial.*

4   Low levels of atmospheric CO_2 between 350–250 million years ago were related to a major period of *organic carbon burial.*

5   An increase in the level of atmospheric CO_2 around 250–125 million years ago may have been due to *increased tectonic outgassing* and partly due to *weathering of organic sediments.*

6   A decline in the level of atmospheric CO_2 over the last approximately 125 million years may be due to *uplifting and weathering of silicates.*

Activity 11.2

There is broad agreement between the results from the paleosol data, Figure A2, and the modelled GEOCARB simulation in Figure 11.14. Further comment on this comparison is contained in the text following this Activity.

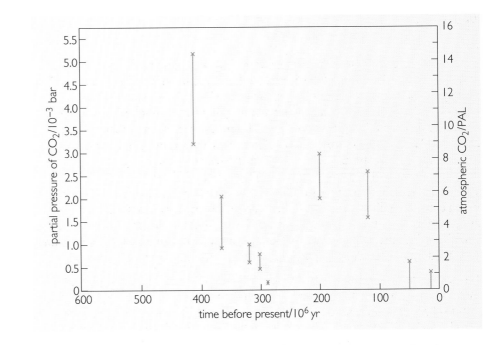

Figure A2
Completed sketch for Activity 11.2.

Acknowledgements

The Course Team wishes to thank the following: Professor Bill Chaloner and Dr Jim Kasting, the external assessors, for providing helpful advice on the content and level of the book; also the student readers Fran Van Wyk de Vries, Peter Daniels, Margaret Deller, Jim Grundy and Colin Whitmore, and the tutor reader Cynthia Burek, for their comments.

Grateful acknowledgement is made to the following sources for permission to reproduce material in this book:

Figures

Cover photograph: NASA, Johnson Space Center; *Preface photograph, Figures 4.2, 11.3, 11.6:* NASA; *Figure 2.1:* adapted from Holland, Heinrich and Petersen, Ulrich. *Living Dangerously The Earth, Its Resources and the Environment.* Copyright © 1995 by PUP. Reprinted by permission of Princeton University Press; *Figure 2.3:* Nerc Satellite Station, Dundee University; *Figure 2.4:* Photos courtesy of Dr J. R. Young, The Natural History Museum, London; *Figure 3.1:* Peter Lewis; *Figures 3.6, 4.3, 4.4, 4.9, 4.10, 4.13, 5.2, 8.8, 10.5, 10.6, 11.4:* Peter Francis; *Figures 3.2, 3.3, 7.1:* T. P. Jones, Cardiff; *Figures 3.4, 11.17, 11.18:* Geoscience Features Picture Library; *Figure 3.5:* Chris Wilson; *Figure 3.7:* Heather Angel/Biofotos; *Figure 3.8:* Reprinted with permission from *Nature*, **333**, Schidlowski, M. 'A 3,800 million-year isotopic record of life from carbon in sedimentary rocks', Copyright 1988 Macmillan Magazines Ltd; *Figures 3.9, 5.3, 5.4:* Reprinted with permission from *Nature*, **359**, Des Marais, D. J. *et al.* 'Carbon isotope evidence for the stepwise oxidation of the proterozoic environment', Copyright 1992 Macmillan Magazines Ltd; *Figure 3.10:* Schidlowski, M. (1982) 'Content and isotopic composition of reduced carbon in sediments', in Holland, H. D. and Schidlowski, M. (eds) *Mineral Deposits and the Evolution of the Biosphere*, Springer-Verlag; *Figure 4.1:* J. Allan Cash Ltd; *Figure 4.5:* Hamersley Iron Pty Ltd; *Figure 4.6:* E. Nisbet, Royal Holloway College; *Figure 4.7:* B. Murton, SOC; *Figures 4.11, 4.12:* Adapted from *Precambrian Research*, **12**, Gay, A. L. and Grandstaff, D. E. 'Chemistry and mineralogy of precambrian paleosols at Elliot Lake, Ontario, Canada', pp 349–373, 1979, with kind permission from Elsevier Science – NL Sara Burgerhartstraat 25, 1055 KV Amsterdam, The Netherlands; *Figure 6.1:* Berner, R. A. and Canfield, D. E. (1989) 'A new model for atmospheric oxygen over phanerozoic time', *American Journal of Science*, **289**, (4). Reprinted by permission of American Journal of Science; *Figure 6.2c:* Dr Miriam Rothschild; *Figure 6.3:* Reprinted with permission from *Nature*, **375**, Graham, J. B. *et al.* 'Implications of the late palaeozoic oxygen pulse for physiology and evolution', Copyright 1995 Macmillan Magazines Ltd; *Figure 6.4a:* Museum of Natural History, Paris; *Figures 6.4b, 11.16:* Natural History Museum, London; *Figure 7.2:* adapted from Holland, H. D. (1991) 'The mechanisms that control the carbon dioxide and oxygen content of the atmosphere', in Schneider, S. H. and Boston, P. J. (eds) *Scientists on Gaia*, MIT Press, © 1991 Massachusetts Institute of Technology; *Figure 7.4:* Abstracted with permission from van Cappellen, P. and Ingall, E. D. 'Redox stabilization of the atmosphere and oceans by phosphorus-limited marine productivity', *Science*, **271**, 26 January 1996. Copyright 1996 American Association for the Advancement of Science; *Figure 8.3:* NASA/GSFC; *Figures 8.4, 8.5, 8.6:* Reprinted with permission from Kerr, J. B. and McElroy, C. T. 'Evidence for large upward trends of ultraviolet-B radiation linked to ozone depletion', *Science*, **262**, 12 November 1993. Copyright 1993 American Association for the Advancement of Science; *Figure 8.9:* G. E. Williams; *Figure 9.1:*

NASA/Bara King; *Figure 10.3:* Reprinted from *Precambrian Research*, **34**, Kasting, J. F., 'Theoretical constraints on oxygen and carbon dioxide concentrations in the precambrian atmosphere', (1987) with kind permission from Elsevier Science – NL Sara Burgerhartstraat 25, 1055 KV Amsterdam, The Netherlands; *Figure 10.4:* Prof. Stephen Moorbath, Oxford; *Figure 10.7:* Kasting, J. F. (1992) 'Proterozoic climates: the effect of changing atmospheric carbon dioxide concentrations', in Schopf, J. W. and Klein, C. (eds) *The Proterozoic Biosphere A Multidisciplinary Study*, Cambridge University Press; *Figure 10.8:* Schopf, J. W. and Klein, C. (1992) *The Proterozoic Biosphere A Multidisciplinary Study*, Cambridge University Press; *Figure 10.9:* Natural Environment Research Council/British Antarctic Survey; *Figure 10.10:* Reprinted with permission from *Nature*, **364**, Jouzel *et al.*, 'Extending the Vostok ice-core record of paleoclimate to the penultimate glacial period.' Copyright 1993 Macmillan Magazines Ltd; *Figure 11.2:* Landform Slides; *Figure 11.5:* Science Photo Library; *Figures 11.8, 11.10, 11.14, 11.19b, 11.20a:* Berner, R. A. (1994) '3 Geocarb II: A revised model of atmosphere CO_2 over phanerozoic time', *American Journal of Science*, **294**, January 1994; *Figure 11.9:* Raymo, M. E. (1991) 'Geochemical evidence supporting T. C. Chamberlain's theory of glaciation', *Geology*, **19**, (4), April 1991; *Figure 11.11:* Popperfoto; *Figure 11.19a:* Adapted from Allegre, C. L. and Schneider, S. H. (1994) 'The evolution of the earth', *Scientific American* , **271**, (4), October 1994. Reproduced by permission of Scientific American, Inc. All rights reserved.